MEASUREMENTS

This book was first published in 1973 for distribution in the United States. Before the end of that decade there were nearly as many copies being sold OUTSIDE the U.S. as inside its borders. Now, a few decades later, it is being sold worldwide.

Consequently in this major revision we have taken great pains to accommodate both of the two major measuring systems in existence. In the book itself, for the most part, we have given both the METRIC (Centigrade, Meter, Second) system of units and the U.S. (as well as Canadian and British to some extents) system.

TABLE B in Chapter 12 has been included to give the reader a very complete reference and comparison between these major systems.

THE
LORE
OF
STILL
BUILDING

By:

Howard & Gibat

If we included the whole body of knowledge on the subject of STILLS and DISTILLation it would require at least a few dozen large volumes to print it all. On the other hand you can carry this book in your pocket and when you finish reading it you'll likely know everything you wanted to now--and probably more!

First Printing - February 1973
Second Printing - August 1973
Reprinted & Revised - December 1978
Fourth Printing - December 1981
Fifth Printing - December 1984
Reprinted & Revised - March 1991
Seventh Printing - January 1992
Eighth Printing - July 1994
Ninth Printing - June 1999
Tenth Printing - March 2012

Printed in U.S.A. by Noguska, LLC
741 North Countyline St.
Fostoria, Ohio 44830-1004
Phone (419) 435-0404
Fax (419) 435-1844

ISBN # 1-88411-1076

CONTENTS
Part I - How to Produce Beverage Alcohols

Part II - How to Produce Fermented & Distilled Fuels

PREFACE

In just a few short hours it will be within your power to construct your own efficient and economical still. You will be able to build a small still for the production of alcoholic beverages or a larger version for the production of a potent liquid fuel. Gasohol is only one of many possible solutions to the fuel shortage explored in this single explosive volume.

Home wine and beer making are both legal in the United States, Canada and Great Britain. Home Distillation (operating a still) is not legal. KNOWING how to distill is not illegal, but sometimes the DOING is!

However, a variance to the Distillation law can be obtained in the United States for the experimenter who wishes to build his own still for producing fuel. This variance does not allow the production of beverage alcohol although there is no chemical difference between the two.

Although it is now illegal to distill at home for your own use there is a very good chance that this part of the law will be changed in the future. The same statutes that govern the tax on alcohol also govern the tax on tobacco. Yet it is not illegal to grow and smoke your own tobacco. This is only one of the many inconsistencies in the law that may very well undergo modernization in the future.

Serious energy shortages have added even greater pressures for the releasing of the legal taboos on the freedom to distill. When such changes are legislated this informational book will then become a valuable textbook to the home distiller.

The information in this book is presented in good faith. To the best of the author's knowledge, it is factual and free from gross error. However, the authors assume no liability for any results or conclusions that may be based in whole or in part on this material. It is presented for informational purposes only.

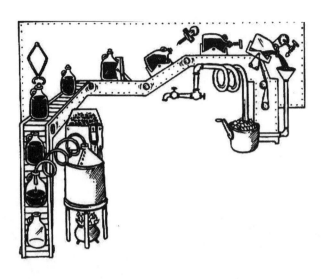

HOW TO PRODUCE BEVERAGE ALCOHOLS

Chapter 1: In The Days Of Yore

In the days of old

I have been told

When alcohol was uninvented:

They fought and maimed.

And killed and lamed.

And in general, stayed discontented!

1-1 In this book we are going to be talking about **Alcohol** (also known more correctly as **Ethanol**). It matters not whether it is in the form of whiskey, wine, beer, vodka, or simply 100 percent pure alcohol. No matter what it is mixed with, brewed in, or distilled out of, the active ingredient in ANY alcoholic drink is, of course, alcohol. And the greater the percentage of alcohol, the more active the ingredient--if not the user--becomes!

PRE-HISTORIC ALCOHOL

1-2   Alcoholic drinks, as we know them today, are a rather recent innovation. Alcoholic drinks, in general, have been with us for as far back as written history exists. Alcohol came into being initially through the simple decomposition of food juices in the presence of yeast and the yeast cells came from the fruit skins or the surrounding air. This process is called **Fermentation** and includes the well known products **Wine** and **Beer**. For a number of reasons the grape plant was probably the first exploited in making wines and then followed other sugary fruit juices. Finally, through a two-step process called "malting" and "mashing", beer was probably introduced. The oldest historical records (from 4000 BC or about 6000 years ago) show the presence of both Wine and Beer - as well as the sporting game of Backgammon.   Beer was not explicitly mentioned, however, until the 6th century BC, as we shall see later.

1-3 Obviously, the alcoholic beverages produced in those earliest of times did not resemble those of today. Sealed and pressurized containers were very rare. Open crock ware was the name of the game. Thus carbonated beverages, such as beer and champagne which require pressurized containers, were not available. Cooling during most of the year was equally unavailable. The beverage relished and fought over would strike modern man as being a cross between sandy mouthwash and much used dishwater. But it did contain Ethyl alcohol, and once past the nose and tongue, it produced the same effect that you and I and the rest of mankind are so familiar with. It is not our purpose at this point to go into the makeup of what is now considered a good wine or beer. This will be dealt with in Chapter 6. Suffice it to say that *Fermented* alcohol did exist in copious quantities from somewhere away back in mankind's gray and misty beginnings. Its palatability was another matter.

HISTORIC ALCOHOL

1-4 By the time the Greeks and Romans came onto the stage (about 500 BC to 0 BC), alcoholic beverages were still confined to wines and beers, but the quality was much improved. The liquid was drained off of its *lees* or *dregs* and containers with crude closures were commonly employed for storage. Some preserving herbs were being used at this time and beverages became palatable.

1-5 The Greeks, of course, had to have a god for everything. The god of fruitfulness (**Dionysus**) was given a face-lifting and emerged as the god of the vine and, hence, of wine. Other names for this same god were Bassareus, Sabazius, and **Bacchus**. The latter name is most often used in modern literature as the god of wine.

1-6 The final step--and a very large one indeed--in the evolution of the alcoholic drink was the discovery of DISTILLATION. Aristotle (380-320 BC) was familiar with distillation as were several others mentioned in writings of the period preceding the middle ages. In 800 BC the Chinese were distilling Rice Beer to obtain a more powerful drink. In Europe, however, no application of distillation was made to Alcoholic beverages until the Arabians introduced the idea into Italy about 1225 AD.

From there the idea slowly spread into Spain, France, and northward into the European countries until it was in popular use by 1650. Oddly enough, the modern Arabians do not drink alcohol as it is forbidden in the Moslem religion by the Koran (Moslem Bible).

EARLY STILL

1-7 It will do well for us to interrupt our story at this point to briefly explain the difference between Fermentation and Distillation. In so doing we will come to understand the actual differences, also, between such diverse drinks as Beer, Wine, Brandy, Whiskey, Vodka, etc.

1-8 FERMENTATION is the term we use to explain the process that takes place when we add yeast to a sugary solution of fruit, vegetable or grain juices. Yeast are small micro-organisms having properties of both plants and animals but generally classified with the plants. The yeast use the sugar in a liquid for food, and in so doing they expel Ethyl Alcohol and Carbon Dioxide as byproducts. The carbon dioxide is given off as a gas and bubbles up through the liquid. The alcohol stays in solution and produces unusual cerebral effects when ingested by animals. In other words it is a narcotic drug. One must avoid becoming emotionally traumatized by the description of alcohol as a narcotic drug. Quite simply a narcotic is any agent that has a soporific, or deadening effect on the brain, or in some pronounced manner alters the mental acuity of the user. Even aspirin can be used as a narcotic.

1-9 ALCOHOL is the name given to a class of compounds containing many members such as **Ethyl** alcohol (Ethanol), **Methyl** alcohol (Methanol),<B> Isopropyl<M> alcohol, etc. Only one of these can be ingested in significant quantities without producing lasting ill effects. This one is Ethyl alcohol which is given off as the byproduct of the Fermentation Process.

1-10   All alcohols are poisonous to varying extents. Some only mildly toxic, such as Ethyl & Isopropyl. Some terribly toxic, such as Methyl alcohol. But Isopropyl alcohol is not intoxicating - that is you can get neither drunk nor "high" on it. It does not affect the brain. **Methyl** alcohol is commonly called wood alcohol since it is easily produced by heating wood (usually logs) in a large closed oven without oxygen. The vapors that are boiled off consist largely of **Methyl alcohol.** **Methyl** alcohol was at one time used in automobile radiators to prevent freezing but has largely been replaced by Ethylene Glycol in recent years. Methyl alcohol is deadly poisonous. **Isopropyl** alcohol is mixed with 30 percent water and sold as Rubbing Alcohol (70 percent Isopropyl). Alcohol types will be discussed more fully in Chapter 3.

1-11   For the time being we need to remember that Ethyl alcohol is the only one that can be drunk safely - in moderate quantities of course because in large quantities it, too, is extremely toxic. Don't forget that and don't let your friends forget it! In Part I of this book the single word Alcohol, by itself, will always mean Ethyl alcohol unless it is further qualified.

1-12 YEAST are tiny microscopic plants that thrive in sugary solutions such as fruit juices. A microscope of 500 to 1000 magnifications is needed to examine them. They sub-divide, or bud, to multiply. Under the right conditions they expel Carbon Dioxide and Alcohol. For making bread the yeast are added to the dough so that the slight fermentation which takes place can introduce Carbon Dioxide bubbles in the bread and, hence, lighten it. For making fermented beverages, the carbon dioxide is usually bubbled off into the surrounding air and only the alcohol and juices are retained.

1-13   Unfortunately the yeast plants cannot go on making alcohol indefinitely. The yeast stagnates when the alcohol percentage in the solution approaches about 16 percent by volume (depending on the yeast variety and techniques employed). The increasing concentration of alcohol renders the yeast cell inoperative and it becomes dormant whether sugar is present or not. The yeast cells simply pollute their environment with alcohol to the extent they can no longer function. In practice an upper limit of about 14% is fairly realistic.

1-14 Now we come to the heart of the matter. All drinkable alcohol is produced initially by the **FERMENTATION** process. This is a rather

**An early still makes use of the cold of winter
for more efficient operation.**

large statement. It includes such things as brandy, vodka, scotch, gin, beer, wine, vermouth and anything else you may wish to mention such as liqueurs, cordials, ad nauseam. The question immediately arises as to how whiskey, say, or gin, both of which contains appreciably more than the upper limit of about 16 percent alcohol, can be obtained from fermentation. Strong liquors (concentrated alcohols) are made from fermented alcoholic beverages (wines and beers) by the process of **Distillation**.

1-15 DISTILLATION, or rectification as it is sometimes called, is the process of separating mixtures or compounds into their constituent parts by a process of heating, evaporating and condensing. It can be put simpler than that by citing an example or two. Sea Water is a mixture of pure water, salt and many minerals. The dissolved solids, such as salt and most minerals, will not evaporate or vaporize to any appreciable extent in normal sunlight, but water will. Thus the heat from the sun shining on the oceans, evaporates or vaporizes huge quantities of pure water, leaving behind most of the solids mentioned. These clouds of vapor travel overland and come into contact with cool air which causes them to condense (or return to the liquid state) and the result is a rainfall of pure water. The pure Water is DISTILLED from sea water in this manner.

1-16 Most liquids with differing boiling points can also be separated in the same manner. As the temperature is raised in a mixed solution one of the liquids will begin evaporating before the other and the resulting vapor, if condensed, will contain more of the liquid with the lowest boiling point. Such a separation will not be nearly so perfect as the first case cited where solids are dissolved in a liquid (sea water) and where separation is almost perfect or very efficient to say the least. In the case of several liquids mixed together, the efficiency of the separation will depend more on how close or how far the boiling points of the liquids are from each other, what their relative concentrations are and the nature of

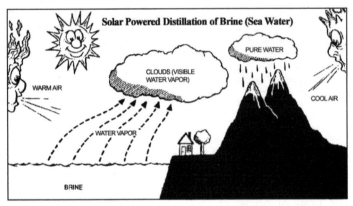

the liquids involved. But nevertheless, in general, a separation can be effected by a process known as **DISTILLATION.**

1-17 Distilled beverages are normally measured in **PROOF** values which in the United States are simply twice the percentage by volume figures. In other words, a beverage that contains 10 percent alcohol by volume is 20 proof in the U.S.A. This is not true in Great Britain or Canada and a comparison set of proof tables is given in Table C (Chapter 12) between all the systems commonly employed. There is no rational reason for employing these different systems of percentages and proofs. They simply evolved over the years. The term proof is said to originate from a method that was used of adding alcoholic liquor to gunpowder and then trying to ignite the powder to establish whether the liquor was "proof" or not. Since alcohol is quite flammable the gunpowder would readily burn if the liquor poured on it did not contain too much water (100 proof). Obviously, such a system would be a rather crude measurement. The term proof is still maintained in modern usage as given in Table C.

Testing for Proof

1-18 We return to the chronological setting of our earlier discussion. We had just introduced the Arabs to the Italians (about 1225 AD) and the Arabs had soon acquainted the Italians with **DISTILLATION**. It took until 1650 to spread all over Europe. Since this is a period of over 400 years, it is apparent that the new methodology did not travel at anywhere near the speed of light. But it wasn't bad speed for the times considering that Europe was in the renaissance during this period and quite disorganized to say the least.

1-19 One of the first products of the new distilling techniques was Brandy, or Cognac as it is sometimes called. The reason for this is that the first STILLS made (from the word diSTILLation) were inefficient. They produced a higher percentage alcoholic drink than was possible with fermentation alone, but did not anywhere approach the efficiency of later stills. A first run through these Stills did little better than double the percentage of alcohol. Thus, instead of a 15 percent wine, the STILL would produce a 30 percent Brandy. By increasing the efficiency of their designs and/or by running the Brandy back through their STILLS again they were able to increase this yield to a 40 to 50 percent Brandy. This is more like the Brandy of today.

1-20 Brandy was THE drink from about 1700 to 1800. Brandy is now distilled out in a single run through a still to 40-55 percent alcohol and stored in Oak barrels for about 5 years before bottling and selling. Initially, it was "aged" only accidentally when an especially good year resulted in more than could be drunk or when barrels might be overlooked for a few years in a dark and little used Wine Celler. When it was noticed that some of this older stock was much improved in

... Must be another Way!

flavor, or at least tasted differently, (the alcoholic percentage stays the same or decreases slightly) the concept of Aging was born.

1-21 Brandy fits into many of the popular scenes that were described for us by writers of that era. A true and touching story concerns one of the greatest mathematicians of all time. He was only 21 years of age and was doomed to fight a duel which he could not win. The night before the duel, he sat down with a beaker of Brandy and committed to paper all that he knew and understood from his researches. The next day he was killed in the duel, and his night's work resulted in the creation of a new branch of mathematics. His name was Evariste Galois and he was killed in Paris, France, on May 31, 1832. So much for Brandy and dueling. Maybe if he hadn't drunk so much brandy he would have won the duel.

Beer

Pliny (023-079) is the earliest writer to mention beer. He declared that Wine was a much preferred drink for Romans

The ancient Egyptians also knew how to make Beer. Herodotus (circa 450 BC) claims that the fermentation from Barley was invented by one of the gods (Isis). Thus the known oldest manufacture of Beer can be ascribed to the Egyptians.

1-22 During the 1800's the supply and quality of Beverage Alcohol increased by leaps and bounds. And the demand increased at least as fast. Alcohol, in many areas such as Kentucky and Tennessee, became a medium of exchange as valuable as money. The more transportable the more valuable it became. Whiskey was born because of the expense of shipping grain from Midwest granaries to eastern markets. The grain (corn, wheat, oats, rye, rice, etc) was converted to a mash, fermented, distilled and shipped for a much greater net profit than otherwise obtainable. We are presently moving in this direction again but for a very different reason: GASOHOL!

1-23 For a variety of reasons, alcohol soon became a very taxable item. It was in high demand and it took equipment and know-how to manufacture in distilled form. In 1792, the first tax was passed on active Stills in the U.S. Then, as now, the accent for taxation fell on the distilled product and not the fermented. Because of the ease of fermenting and concealment it is not difficult to understand why the line was drawn at distillation. The first tax laws allowed stills under 400 gallons to either pay an annual tax or, if they did not operate continuously, a monthly tax, based on the schedule of operation. From 1815 to 1862 it was a tranquil period. During this time there were no taxes on any alcoholic beverages, distilled or otherwise. The Civil War, and its needs for revenue, re-instituted the liquor tax which has not been off the books since.

1-24 The tax in 1862 was 20 cents per gallon of proof liquor (100 proof or 50 percent alcohol). A mere pittance. As with all taxes, there seemed but one direction to go with the passage of time - UP! In 1864 it was reset at 60 cents per proof gallon. Except for some brief excursions during the latter years of the Civil War, the tax stayed relatively constant until 1900, by which time it had risen to $1.10 per gallon; $3.20 in 1917; then down to $2.00 in 1934 after the repeal of the 18th amendment (prohibition). By 1951, this had risen to $10.50.

1-25 At the present time it costs about $200.00 to pay for the wholesale costs on a 55 gallon barrel of 200 proof Ethyl Alcohol - but the Federal taxes you must pay before you can call it your own amount to about $1,000.00!! This, of course, is before any state or local taxes are added. Alcohol and Tobacco are the only two items that have had a continuous excise tax since the Civil War.

ALCOHOLIC EXCESSES

1-26 The 1800's brought forth a drastic change in the public's attitudes toward alcoholic beverages. The relaxed and easy-going early 1800's gave way to the very intemperate Temperance Societies in the late 1800's. By 1900 an ugly mood was evident throughout the United States. The temperance movements started in Maine with the passage of one of the first sweeping prohibitory laws in the nation. Before long, however, the real strength of the movement shifted to the Midwest and the south where it remains to this day. It is easy for us to look back and regard those in the forefront of such movements as being narrow and bigoted. It is easy but it would be unjustified.

1-27 By the latter half of 1800, the industrial sectors of the world were plagued with alcoholism on an alarming scale. The pathetic tales of poorly dressed little waifs shivering in the cold trying to get their fathers to come home from a saloon were a little overdrawn. But Alcoholism was on the increase as industrialization spread. Even fishermen out on the high seas were not immune. In the North Sea, between England and the European Continent the seas were filled with floating saloons. Special legislation was needed to control the situation.

1-28 The United States in 1900 was emerging as the most powerful nation in the world. But as the nation grew ever larger and more complex so also did its internal problems.

Chapter 2: Post Yore Days

TEMPERANCE MOVEMENTS

2-1 Chapter one dealt briefly with the subject of potable (drinkable) alcohol as it was known to mankind up through about 1900. By this time the casual approach to the drinking of alcohol was commencing to be replaced by the critical and condemnatory. Definite and different points of view were emerging. Each individual, of course, maintained a view that was the result of the sum total of his or her experience to that time.

2-2 These personal experiences were colored by the occupation of the individual citizen. The lawyer, though he might enjoy drinking was brought into daily contact with the consequences of over-drinking. The tax collector saw it as merely another commodity used to support the necessary activities of the State. The religiously inclined, in spite of the manifold biblical references to wine, were also brought into daily contact with its misuses. Social groups could not ignore the impact of excessive drinking on their own local life styles. Such groups as the W.C.T.U. (Women's Christian Temperance Movement) and the Salvation Army bridged the gap between social and religious concerns and took an activist part in either discouraging drinking or picking up the pieces from the consequences of its misuse.

2-3 Pendulums have a way of swinging in both directions--but never simultaneously. In spite of efforts by President Roosevelt (Theodore not Franklin), Taft and Wilson in the first two decades of 1900, the handwriting was on the wall. The complexion of succeeding sessions of Congress became increasingly prohibitory where alcohol was concerned.

2-4 It is characteristic of the American political system to over-react and to legislate against the symptoms while ignoring the causes. It did not act uncharacteristically in this crisis. The Supreme Court fell into line and approved some very questionable legislation as being constitutional (Webb-Kenyon Interstate Commerce Amendment Bill vetoed by President Taft, the Jones-Randall amendment, the Reed amendment, etc).

2-5 Local states and cities were voting themselves dry in attempts to solve the problem on their own. Their plight was understandable and while the solutions they proposed were hardly laudable, their options were strictly limited. The Federal Government had the only power available that could provide the national sense of purpose needed.

2-6 Instead of assuming that those who trafficked in liquor or that those who drank it were simply "bad", some questions needed to be asked concerning the quality or desirability of our social structures as they had evolved to that time. What caused so many of our fellow citizens and toilers to prefer stupefaction to cooperation? We face the same problem today with drinking and with drugs in general and, again, the right questions are never asked; systems are easier targets.

2-7 As a point of comparison wine and beer are commonly sold at many restaurants along the major highway systems in Europe. Not at little taverns, by the way, but in major restaurants along the major freeway systems that are built and controlled by the Federal Governments. There is no public outcry against it and there is no highway carnage resulting from it. Why?

2-8 For one thing, in most of these countries, it is generally not thought commendable and "fun" to drink oneself to a stupor; followed by wretched vomiting and nausea; followed by another day or two of headaches and severely reduced mental and physical abilities. In the United States such actions are portrayed in the most popular movies as being normal and acceptable behavior; perhaps even funny and macho.

2-9 Every society has a small sampling of individuals who cannot or will not control their basest, self-destructive tendencies. What is there in the American Psyche that causes a great many, perhaps a majority, of young persons (and unfortunately many older ones who never outgrow it) to consider such destructive and debasing actions to be fun and desirable? Compared to what??

2-10 Rather than trying to answer such obviously difficult questions the easy and popular solution (legislators ALWAYS take the easy or popular way--and who can blame them?) is to cry loudly and emphatically for the building of more jails for more felons who must serve longer sentences.

2-11 It is a country which views itself with pride as a caring society; so caring it is afraid to discipline its young, pushing them into the mainstream of society at age 18 with few social responsibilities and many social demands. It is a country which has gradually shifted to becoming an uncaring

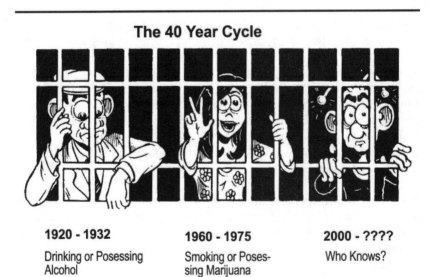

The 40 Year Cycle

1920 - 1932

Drinking or Posessing Alcohol

1960 - 1975

Smoking or Posessing Marijuana

2000 - ????

Who Knows?

society which is not afraid to--sometimes is even proud to-- award draconian prison terms when its own unfettered waifs collide with the solid walls of reality.

PROHIBITION

2-12 The 18th Amendment was passed by the necessary two thirds vote in the Senate on August 1, 1917 by a vote of 65 to 20. On December 17, 1917, it passed the House by a vote of 228 to 128. The necessary two thirds state approval was obtained on January 16, 1919. One year later, on January 16, 1920, National Prohibition commenced in the United States. The Volstead Act was passed by Congress on October 28, 1919 to provide for drastic enforcement. It was vetoed by President Wilson but was passed over this veto. From January 16, 1920 to December 5, 1933, it was not legal to manufacture, sell, transport, import or export beverage liquor in the United States of America. The "Noble Experiment" had begun!

2-13 During Prohibition, the repressive legislation passed and judicial actions taken remind one very much of the recent drug problem. The situations are so clearly similar that it causes pause for wondering if our collective intelligence as a nation hasn't peaked out. Cars were searched for alcohol and if a passenger had alcohol on him or her, even if unbeknownst to the driver, the car and all personal possessions in it were confiscated and sold by the State. As an isolated example, a lawyer named S.S. Holt was shot and killed on his way home from arguing a case in the United States District Court in Raleigh, North Carolina on June 1, 1925. The officer shooting him dead stated that Holt stopped his car for a moment along the roadside and thus he, the officer, thought Mr. Holt was carrying liquor in the car. This turned out to be totally unfounded. Mr. Holt was killed without warning and in the presence of the Chief of Police.

2-14 Paid informers were hired to infiltrate groups and encourage them to buy alcohol illegally so that the "culprits" could be arrested by the State Authorities. Constitutional liberties were set aside if the question of alcohol arose - and the community approved. Does all this sound familiar?

2-15 Such petty and demeaning acts on the part of the Federal and State governments invited the contempt of the governed. And the invitation was readily accepted. The pocket whiskey flask came into vogue as a safe way to carry whiskey. Meanwhile the unresolved national problems which precipitated the crisis in the first place were simply becoming worse and we entered into the worst depression in our history.

It is interesting to note that the 1920's decade brought forth the first nationwide experiments into "permissive" behavior patterns when discipline of any kind was likened to immorality or even bestiality. The more things change the more they stay the same.

REPEAL

2-16 Finally, in 1932, the simmering revolt against the 18th Amendment and the Volstead Act entered into the presidential campaign pitting Roosevelt against Hoover. The 21st Amendment repealed the 18th Amendment and was ratified on December 5, 1933. National Prohibition was dead.

2-17 We were rescued temporarily from our profound lack of a cogent national purpose by the self-preservation instincts during the 1930's and 40's. War engulfed the world and allowed us to look the other way for another two decades. When we looked back, we were astonished to find that our problems had not gone away.

AFTER REPEAL

2-18 Although the 21st Amendment repealed Prohibition, by no means did it mean the end of government intervention and control of liquor. The State governments now assume the task of regulating the liquor traffic but the Federal Government keeps for itself many prime controlling functions. Licensing and inspecting of plants or firms having anything to do with the manufacture, importation or distillation of alcohol is a Federal prerogative. Federal regulations lay out the entire foundation and framework within which the liquor industry is compelled to operate.

2-19 Most of the Federal Government's regulations are set forth to insure that tax payments cannot be easily avoided. The state regulations are more often colored by local prejudices and mores but are also laid out in such a manner as to insure that the proper tax revenues are collected.

State taxes and controls vary widely and are usually moderate in scope and tone. It is worth noting, however, that the Federal statutes are not moderate. You cannot obtain a license for distilling for your own use. You cannot build a Still even for purifying water, unless you register it with the Federal government and you cannot obtain a license to distill in a home or anything close to resembling one. However it has become easier in recent years to obtain a license for experimental distillation and for the production of alcohol to be used as a fuel, (Gasohol, primarily).

2-20 While this all may sound oppressive, and undoubtedly is, these laws can and may be modified in future years. If you suggest such a modification to your local representative or senator, you should be prepared to answer one question: If this tax source is eliminated, where are the several billion dollars in revenue that liquor taxes produce each year going to come from??

OTHER COUNTRIES

2-21 In Canada the Scott Act is used to determine whether an area will be wet or dry. The British, in general, have a more relaxed legal attitude towards liquor than does the United States. The Canadian laws operate about midway between those of their U.S. neighbors and the British Commonwealth. The United States is the only western country to have experimented with National Prohibition. Saudi Arabia enforces a National Prohibition policy because the majority of its people are of the Islam religion (Moslems) which, itself, prohibits the drinking of alcoholic beverages. Similarly with the rest of the world, however, this does not prevent a large proportion of good Muslims from drinking; as with any artificially proscribed article it is simply done carefully.

2-22 Thus, while the average citizen in the United States might imagine that all of the old "Pot Still" methods now in existence came from the hills of Kentucky or Arkansas, it is just as likely that at least part of the methodology originated in the frozen tundra of a northern Canadian Province or on the hot sands of the Rub' al-Khali desert in the southern Arabian peninsula--as a matter of fact
some of it did!

2-23 And so here we are in the Post Yore Days. And in spite of all the troubles we have there are at least two positive things that can be said about our present situation: It certainly is an interesting time to be alive and thank God we got our alcohol back!!

Chapter 3: Fundamentals of Alcohol

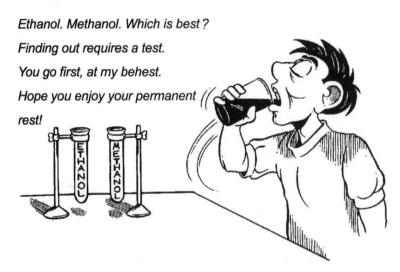

Ethanol. Methanol. Which is best?

Finding out requires a test.

You go first, at my behest.

Hope you enjoy your permanent

rest!

FIRST FUNDAMENTALS

3-1 This is the "technical" chapter. If you have only a little difficulty with this chapter then struggle through as it will help your understanding immensely. If you find it extremely difficult then skim through the difficult portions and read the rest. Be assured that you can still understand completely the rest of this book without this chapter!

3-2 Heretofore we have been following the usual practice in the everyday world of grossly misusing the word alcohol. Alcohol is really the family name for a whole group of compounds with widely varying characteristics. Ethyl alcohol, or grain alcohol, is properly called Ethanol. We shall use Ethanol primarily from this point forward when discussing Ethyl alcohol. This chapter delves into some of the interesting facts about all the alcohols with the emphasis on Ethanol, of course. There are many things about the alcohols you might find surprising. The more you know about this fascinating narcotic the better you will be able to use it to your life.

CHEMISTRY OF ALCOHOL

3-3 The word Chemistry alarms some people almost as much as the word Sex bothers others. Neither word will bother you in this book as we are not going to say enough about the former to make you unhappy nor enough about the latter to make you happy.

3-4 The two great subdivisions of chemistry are Organic and Inorganic. Although the distinctions no longer mean much of anything, they were devised when chemists were first trying to put some order into what we must all agree is a very disordered world. Organic compounds were originally thought to be concerned solely with life processes. All of these contain Carbon whose chemical symbol is "C". Carbon is found in all life processes - whether animal or plant. Thus all compounds with carbon fall into the broad class of Organic compounds. Coal and Oil are two of the most important members of this broad group of Organic Compounds. If the organic compound contains Carbon and Hydrogen (symbol for Hydrogen is H) together, it is called a Hydrocarbon. Coal, Oil and Natural Gas are all Hydrocarbons.

3-5 A single molecule of Carbon is denoted by C alone. Two molecules by C2; three by C3 etc. This system of numbering the molecules of any element is applied to all the elements.

3-6 The Hydrocarbons are found to be composed of almost all conceivable combinations of Carbon and Hydrogen. Some Hydrocarbons contain one Carbon atom (C) and four Hydrogen atoms (H4). This is written as CH4. Others are C5H8, and there are even huge groups such as C100H202. In order to organize these more logically, chemists arrange these molecules according to their size. Out of all the possible combinations, several groupings of order are made. One of the first discovered, by our friends the chemists, is a group whose symbols and names are, in ascending order.

Oil and water are known not to mix.

But Oil and Alcohol will do so.

The problem is how you can fix.

The terrible taste of the two-so.

TABLE I	
ALKANE series of the **ALIPHATIC** hydrocarbons	
CH_4	Methane
C_2H_6	Ethane
C_3H_8	Propane
C_4H_{10}	Butane
C_5H_{12}	Pentane
Etc.	Etc.

3-7 As you have probably guessed the list could go on almost forever as the molecules get larger and larger. As you might have also guessed, the first listed are the lightest. The first few are light gases, then heavy gases, then liquids, then thick liquids (such as tar) and finally solids. The names of most of these compounds are probably familiar. Methane is the explosive gas found in many coal mines. Propane and Butane are sold under great pressure, in tanks, for home and farm usage.

3-8 Chemists have a way of never letting well enough alone. Having discovered these rather unusual and never ending chains of molecules, it was further found that by making slight changes in the structural formulas other non-ending groups of compounds could be accurately described. For instance the first member is Methane, CH_4. By substituting what is known as a Hydroxyl group (one atom of Oxygen and one of Hydrogen - OH) for one of the Hydrogen atoms in Methane a new stable compound is formed whose formula is CH_3OH. By making the same substitution into the entire Alkane series above, we get a brand new series:

TABLE II *Aliphatic ALCOHOLS*	
CH_3OH	Methanol (Methyl Alcohol)
C_2H_5OH	Ethanol (Ethyl Alcohol)
C_3H_7OH	Propanol (Isopropyl Alcohol)
Etc.	Etc.

3-9 Although this process of substituting and renaming could and does go on for some time, we can recognize our destination and this is where we get off. The first member is wood alcohol, the second is beverage alcohol, the third is rubbing alcohol. Only the second is of real interest to us.

3-10 Notice that there are two systems of naming the alcohols. Such a double system of naming is one of the unusual features of organic chemistry. Both are correct. However, in recent years it has become more common to use the so-called systematic names such as Methanol, Ethanol, etc. This is because many people, in their rush to oblivion, failed utterly to pay heed to anything but the name alcohol. As a consequence some Methyl Alcohol has been drunk mistakenly for Ethyl Alcohol. Methanol is a deadly poison...oblivion comes ahead of schedule!

3-11 As a point of interest, Isopropyl, or rubbing alcohol, is very little more toxic than Ethanol, but unfortunately for the beverage hound, it is not intoxicating either. As mentioned before, its primary usage is as an antiseptic and in a 70 percent solution with water, as a liniment to be rubbed on sore muscles (rubbing alcohol).

PROPERTIES OF ETHANOL (ETHYL ALCOHOL)

3-12 Table II shows the first few members of the Aliphatic Alcohols. You would expect that they have some similar properties or what would be the use in grouping them together? On the other hand, you would expect some dissimilar properties or what would be the use of giving them different names? So far as similarities are concerned, most have a pleasant odor and they enter into similar reactions with other chemicals. In other respects they are loners.

As we have learned, Methanol is very toxic, Ethanol slightly toxic and Isopropyl only slightly more toxic than Ethanol. Only Ethanol is both non-toxic and intoxicating - which is a study in contradictions!! Two other alcohols worthy of mention are Ethylene Glycol (used as anti-freeze and Glycerol, or glycerin).

3-13 It is also worth noting that ALL of the alcohols are TOXIC if ingested in large amounts. Likewise very tiny amounts of any of the alcohols are hardly toxic at all. But very tiny means something like eyedropper amounts. The fixed rule for beverage alcohol is to stay away from any alcohols excepting Ethanol and never, never drink yourself into a stupor or associate with those who do. Stupor and Stupid differ by very little as we can see. Alcohol for fuel is another matter. Methanol, for instance, makes a great fuel.

LET ME SEE... TODAY I GUESS I WILL DISCOVER ADIABETIC TRI-ANGULATED MORPHISTOLOGY!

3-14 Pure Ethanol boils at a temperature of 172.9 degrees Fahrenheit or 78.3 degrees Centigrade at sea level. In this text we are not going to be much concerned about pure Ethanol. In our experience, the Ethanol will be mixed with a mass of other materials, some liquid, some starches, and some compounds which defy accurate description. Thus, it is more useful for us to determine how a mixture of ethanol and water behaves as we will encounter this situation by far the oftenest. Wine and Beer are both very close to being a simple mixture of water and Ethanol.

3-15 When two different liquids are mixed together, all sorts of things can happen. One liquid can float on top of the other such as with oil and water.

An immediate explosion can occur such as with a strong acid and base mixture. The combination can take up heat (endothermic) or it can give off heat (exothermic). The two can remain independent of each other totally (a mixture) or they can exist semi-independently where they share the common spaces and remain everywhere homogeneous (a solution) or they can chemically combine to form brand new compounds.

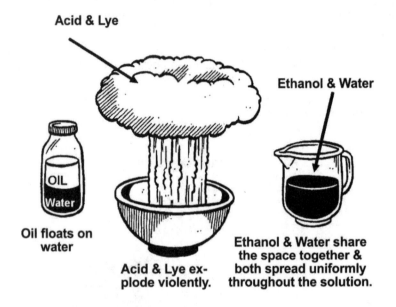

Acid & Lye

Ethanol & Water

Oil floats on water

Acid & Lye explode violently.

Ethanol & Water share the space together & both spread uniformly throughout the solution.

3-16 Ethanol and water are in the middle class. They mix uniformly in all proportions and a small amount of heat is given off when they are so mixed. The volume of the solution is also a little less than the sum of their original volumes. 52 volumes of alcohol mixed with 48 volumes of water, combine to make 96 volumes of solution instead of the anticipated sum of 100. They are said to be Miscible in each other, meaning that they can mix in all proportions without one or the other settling out or becoming saturated. But they do not, in general, form a chemical bond. Share and share alike is their motto.

3-17 Because of this loose sharing arrangement Ethanol cannot be re-separated from water without a little effort. For instance, it cannot simply be poured off the top as an oil and water mixture could. On the other hand, it does not require the enormous effort it would take to break a chemical bond. For the present it is enough to know that through the process of Distillation we can effect a very good separation.

DISTILLATION

3-18 From the engineering point of view, distillation can become a complex thing. But in theory and in general practice, it is nothing more nor less than boiling a mixture of liquids in the hope that one or the other will boil off first. If one does it can be collected as steam, cooled to condense it back to a liquid and, hence, separated. It actually works. And, as can be expected, it works better with some solutions and poorer with others. In the next few paragraphs we will discuss in some detail the actions that take place when we boil two different liquids together. It will make your understanding of the following chapter easier and, perhaps, you may even find it interesting.

3-19 If it is desired to separate two totally miscible liquids, that are in solution together, it can be done by boiling distillation if and only if they do not form an Azeotrope. An Azeotrope is a mixture of substances all of which boil at the same temperature (constant boiling temperature). The worst that we can say about azeotropes is that they are difficult to spell or pronounce. Any pure substance, such as water, boils at a constant temperature until the last drop is gone. Most liquids in their pure state follow this same rule and it is safe to say that there are few substances, indeed, with exactly the same boiling point. So it would seem that we are spending valuable time and paper on a rather rare phenomena.

3-20 A great many solutions with different boiling points do form azeotropes and Ethanol and water is one of these. Fortunately for us there is only one critical concentration of Ethanol and water

TABLE III
Variation of Boiling Point with Concentration of Ethanol in Water

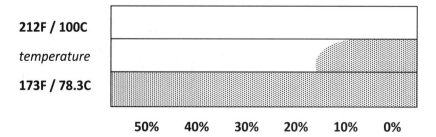

212F / 100C					
temperature					
173F / 78.3C					
50%	40%	30%	20%	10%	0%

which forms an azeotrope and even more fortunately this concentration is almost pure Ethanol with very little water. The azeotropic concentration for Ethanol and water is 97.2 percent Ethanol (this would be 194.4 proof!). Below this concentration, say for instance a 50-50 mixture, the solution boils at or very close to the temperature of Ethanol (about 173F or 78.3C degrees at sea level) until all of the Ethanol is boiled off, at which time there is a sharp rise in the boiling point to that of water (212F or 100C degrees). Table III shows this.

3-21 Because both liquids have some vapor pressure, there will always be a little water going into vapor (steam) along with the Ethanol. But until the point is reached where less than 10 percent of the Ethanol exists, most of the vapor is Ethanol. The substance being heated or boiled in a distillation is called the **Residue** and the boiled off portion is the **Distillate**.

3-22 After a first distillation the Distillate should be at least double its initial percentage. The percentage alcohol in the Distillate is going to depend on its percentage in the Residue before distillation began; on the skill of the operator; and on the efficiency of the still.

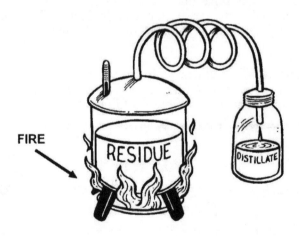

Starting with the typical mash of, perhaps, 10 percent alcohol, a first run on a simple still might yield a Distillate of about 30 percent alcohol. To increase this percentage higher, the obvious procedure would be to run the distillate through the still again...and again...and again, until the desired percentage is reached.

3-23 When this is done, the distillate DOES NOT get closer and closer to 100 percent Ethanol. It approaches 97.2 percent Ethanol. This is because at 97.2 percent the solution becomes constant boiling (azeotropic) and the amount of Ethanol in the vapor is exactly 97.2 percent which leaves the residue the same and it keeps right on boiling at the same old temperature. This temperature, by the way, is 78.2C or 172F degrees. It is just a trifle less than the boiling point of pure Ethanol alone (less than a degree).

3-24 For the curious, this unusual feature is a result of the deviation of the mixture from a so-called "ideal" solution. In an ideal solution each molecule intermixes freely and totally with its foreign neighbors but in no wise becomes associated with them in any chemical bonds. The result is a perfectly homogeneous solution with each component of the solution being evenly distributed throughout the solution in direct proportions to its proportion in the total solution. Some time back we mentioned that when alcohol and water are mixed together, a slight amount of heat is generated (the solution is exothermic). If this were a detective novel we would remind you that you had received the vital clue to the solution (no-pun intended).

3-25 The heat release indicates that on the atomic level there is some hanky panky going on. Some Ethanol molecules are playing around with the water molecules and forming some loose bonds. These loose associations are disturbing the homogeneity of the solution - don't they always - and the result is a slight alteration of the vapor pressure (boiling point) of the combined liquids. This, in turn, causes the solution to become azeotropic just before the point at which it would be pure Ethanol.

3-26 This has several consequences. Pure Ethanol is rarely sold on the open market. If you buy an uncut (undiluted) grain alcohol at the liquor store, it will be 190 proof (95 percent) rather than 200 proof. This is below the azeotropic concentration. There are other ways to achieve 100 percent Ethanol, but it is hardly worth the bother as far as beverage alcohol is concerned. The extra 5 percent would increase the cost and nobody, but nobody, drinks Ethanol in anywhere near that concentration anyhow. So far as fuel operations are concerned it is often good enough to take the solution up to the 97% point since above that point little or no pure water exists anymore.

3-27 On the other hand if it is necessary to obtain 100% Ethanol for fuel operations there are some good methods available. Anyone operating a conventional still must be made aware that it is futile to try to achieve a greater concentration than 97.2 percent. To get a 100% concentration such things as Entrainers must be added to your alcohol.

In this case the process is every bit as formidable as the word. Who wants to add such things as benzene to their expensive alcohol just to get another few percentage points of purity? Have you ever tasted benzene?? But, if the end result is NOT to drink but to BURN, then the addition of entrainers to the nearly pure product is the way to go.

3-28 Cut and **Uncut** are two terms you will run across occasionally. They indicate respectively, **Dilute** and **Undiluted**. The **Diluent** used is nearly always water or juices. A diluent is an inactive additive used to dilute (cut).

MEASUREMENT OF ETHANOL

3-29 The amount of alcohol in the **Distillate** can be easily measured with a P&T (Proof & Tralle or simply Proof) Hydrometer.

3-30 A Hydrometer, as used in alcoholic measurements, is a long, thin, hollow and sealed tube, usually glass. Archimedes was the first one to have discovered the principle of the hydrometer which is that any object floated in a liquid floats at such a point that the liquid displaced by the submerged part of the object is exactly equal to the weight of the whole object.

3-31 Wood floats on water because it weighs less for the space it occupies than an equivalent amount of water. If we place a small weight on a floating block of wood, it sinks into the water enough to compensate for the extra weight. The pressure pushing down on the water is exactly balanced by the pressure of the water upward on the object. We call this concept of

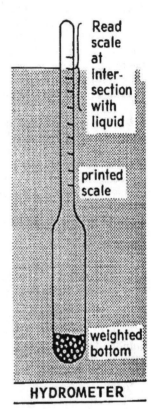

Read scale at Inter- section with liquid

printed scale

weighted bottom

HYDROMETER

Hydrometer Principal:

The submerged part of the block displaces an amount of water that weighs exactly the same as the entire block. Discovered by Archimedes.

weight per space occupied the **Density** of the object or medium. If the Density of an object is greater than that of water (such as a rock or iron bar), it sinks.

3-32 Because water is so common in the world pure water is used as the reference medium in measuring density and is given a value of one (1). Density, when compared to water in this manner is also referred to as Specific Gravity. Thus, if something has a density of 8, such as iron, this means that it is 8 times as dense or 8 times as heavy as the same amount of water. Common sand has a density of 2.3 and therefore is 2.3 times as heavy as water (or 230 percent). Oak has a density of .71 and therefore is only .71 (or 71 percent) as heavy as water. Ethanol has a density of .79 or is 79 percent as heavy as water.

3-33 Since Ethanol is lighter than water, but doesn't really float in water, the obvious result of mixing Ethanol and water is to alter its density. Thus, a solution of Ethanol and water will have a density between .79 (pure Ethanol) and 1.0 (pure water).

3-34 A P&T hydrometer has scales to read off the Specific Gravity or Density in units of either Proof (twice the percent of alcohol by volume) or Tralle (percentage of alcohol by volume).

3-35 It is not nearly so easy to measure the alcoholic percentage of fermented juices. These contain much dissolved foreign material such as starches, sugars, microscopic bits and pieces of fruit or grain particles,

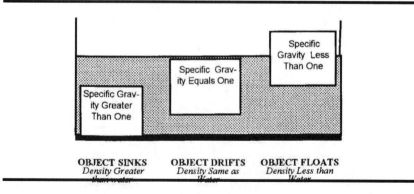

OBJECT SINKS	OBJECT DRIFTS	OBJECT FLOATS
Density Greater than water	*Density Same as Water*	*Density Less than Water*

DENSITY

(Weight per given volume)

etc. This solid material in suspension alters the gravity reading in an unpredictable fashion as the solid content of fruits or grains are never exactly, or even approximately, the same from fruit to fruit. This need not concern us unduly. Only rarely, if ever, will we want to know the original alcoholic content of the fermented mash or juice. It will either have fermented completely or not and there are easy ways to tell one way or the other. And after fermented mash has run through the still at least once, it can be measured accurately with a P&T Hydrometer from that point onward.

3-36 One method of measuring the alcoholic content of a freshly fermented juice or mash is to remove a liquid sample of a pint or so and distill out Exactly half of this sample in a small still. This distillate will contain all (or nearly all) of the alcohol, will be free from contaminants for the most part, and can be measured with a P&T Hydrometer. Take half of the reading obtained in this manner to find the alcoholic content of the batch from which the sample was removed. For instance, if the hydrometer shows a proof of 40 in the distillate then the original sample, before distilling must have had an alcoholic content of half this amount, or a proof of 20 (10 percent alcohol by volume).

3-37 Hydrometers with different scales are needed to measure wines and beers. Another type of Ethanol measuring device is a Vinometer. This is a thin glass tube, smaller than a hydrometer. A Vinometer uses the change in surface tension of an Ethanol and water solution to yield its measurement.

One Method of Determining the Original

Remove a small portion of the mash (pint or quart, for instance).

Distill out exactly half of this sample.

Check the distillate with a P&T Hydrometer. The alcoholic percentage of the original mash is half of this value.

It has few things to recommend it, but it does take very little Ethanol to perform this measurement (a few drops) and it can be done quickly. It has been reported in some literature to be inaccurate while other sources suggest that if the tubing is wet down first with some diluted Ethanol and then cleared out completely, it performs very well. Vinometers are also used to determine alcohol content of dry, or nearly dry, wines.

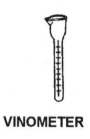

VINOMETER

PRODUCTION & THE USES OF ETHANOL

3-38 Fermentation is the best known source for Ethanol and throughout most of the world it is the only source. In the Unites States, however, it accounts for only about 20 to 25 percent of the total output. The rest is made synthetically from Ethylene, a hydrocarbon. The synthetic alcohol so produced is used industrially for the most part. The only liquid solvent with more usages than alcohol is water! The production of varnishes, shellac, plastics and smokeless gunpowder are all dependent on alcohols in one form or another.

DENATURED ALCOHOL

3-39 There are many industrial uses for Ethanol as has been pointed out. Because of the tax rate, its cost would make it too expensive to use. The government does not want to lose valuable tax dollars by giving workers in a plant access to cheap Ethanol. There are several alternatives. If the manufacturer must have pure Ethanol, such as for an additive to food colorings, then the government requires that the manufacturer keep strict and exact accounting of each and every drop that comes into his possession. This can be a tremendous bother and is costly to the manufacturer, but in some cases is unavoidable.

3-40 In most cases, the alcohol does not need to be pure so long as it does not contain certain harmful products to the manufacturing process for which it is needed. For use in these cases, the government keeps a list of 50 or so different and specialized additives to add to the Ethanol to ruin it for beverage purposes. This process is called **Denaturing,** and these types of denaturants are termed **SD** for Special Denaturants. One such of these is Acetaldehyde.

3-41 In other cases, the type of additive has a much wider latitude. In these cases, the government keeps two CD formulas (for Completely Denatured) on hand. Methyl alcohol and Benzene are used in those formulas as fouling agents.

3-42 These fouling agents are both deadly poisons. Thus the Federal Government is put in the uncomfortable position of intentionally poisoning Ethanol and thereby inadvertently causing a few deaths each year. It is much akin to a householder keeping a shotgun handy for burglars even though it is understood that this same action by all householders is going to result in a few burglars being shot (and possibly killed) each year.

PHYSIOLOGICAL ASPECTS OF ETHANOL

3-43 In this section we will say a few words about you and your Ethanol and what effects you have on each other as you share the same body. Ethanol is used by the body as a fuel in the same manner as sugar. It is ultimately broken down into Carbon Dioxide and water. However, its absorption rate is very slow. You can absorb about a tablespoon of pure Ethanol per hour, but this varies widely according to individual disposition, energy output, and size. In other words if you are working very hard and are overweight you can drink more alcohol, without feeling any harmful effects, than an underweight, lethargic person.

3-44 Ethanol causes the outside skin temperatures to rise and the internal organ temperature to drop. This is a very bad combination if you are going to be exposed to generally cold conditions. It is the opposite of what would be desirable. You can freeze to death in a hurry. Ethanol is toxic and acts as a mild poison. When you drink it faster than it can be assimilated it builds up in the bloodstream and depresses the central nervous system. Thus it is a depressant or "downer" as they are sometimes called. The difference in concentration levels that your body can tolerate is about 4 to 1. That is, at levels of about 1 Part Per Thousand (PPT or .1 percent) you are barely conscious of its presence. At 4 PPT you would be in an alcoholic coma which could easily be fatal. At points in between you are in between.

3-45 Ethanol is present in your body at all times. It is a natural by-product of some bodily functions. Its natural level is, however, quite low. It is interesting to note that because of its toxicity to living organisms, the alcohols in general are used as antiseptics. Isopropyl alcohol is commonly employed for this. As the concentration is increased the antiseptic properties improve markedly until a concentration of 70 percent is reached after which its antiseptics powers Decrease. This is a rather unexpected departure and this is why the common Isopropyl alcohol sold as rubbing alcohol is commonly marketed in a 70 percent by volume mixture.

3-46 Ethanol is primarily metabolized in the liver. This is why the misuse of Ethanol so often results in Cirrhosis of the liver. Ethanol is high in calories and is easily absorbed from the digestive tract into the bloodstream. But, unlike carbohydrates and fats, it cannot be readily stored in the tissues, it can scarcely be disposed of through the kidneys or lungs, and cannot be oxidized by normal body tissues. Thus this high energy substance enters the body and cannot be simply discarded - as many substances can - but must be burned up and this "burning" can only be accomplished in the liver. The liver, alone, contains the necessary enzymes for breaking the alcohol down into carbon dioxide and water.

3-47 The liver of the average healthy person has no difficulty in metabolizing moderate amounts of Ethanol. Excessive drinking in spurts can cause the liver to generate and store fats as a result of this high metabolization. These fats, however, are a reversible condition

'bout time we changed the muffler Henry, it's backfiring again!

and would normally be washed away in the bloodstream when the high alcoholic ingestion ceased. Continued excessive drinking - as in the case of an alcoholic - leads to Hepatitis (death of some liver cells) and then cirrhosis (fibrous scars in the interconnecting tissues of the liver which interfere with the liver's ability to function).

3-48 The lesson here in Not that Ethanol is harmful. Like most other things we eat or drink the human body appears to have no difficulty in adapting itself to a moderate intake of Ethanol. Too much fat in our diet causes atheriosclerosis and results in heart attacks. Too much sitting around brings on gout. Too much alcohol harms the liver. The lesson is that moderation in all things is much to be desired.

FLASH POINTS OF ETHANOL

3-49 Determining the flash point of a combustible liquid can be dangerous so you would be ill-advised to try it. But the procedure is quite simple. The liquid to be tested is heated until the temperature is reached at which the surface of the liquid ignites when a match is held close to it. The temperature at which the surface can be ignited is the Flash Point. To find the flash points of oils, they are usually immersed in sand (for safety's sake) and then heated gradually while a thermometer reading is taken and a flame held close to the surface of the hot sand. In the case of gasoline no heat is needed. It is already above the flash point at room temperature. So is pure Ethanol whose flash point is 51 degrees F. But the flash point for 90 proof ethanol (Whiskey or Vodka straight from the bottle) is 78 degrees F or 26 degrees C.

3-50 All of this to say that precautions must be taken around any still and its distillate.   Especially when the liquids are hot and highly concentrated. Common sense precautions need to be observed but one need not be paranoid about it.   A fire extinguisher should always be handy and everybody should know how to use it. No smoking should be allowed on still premises. That sort of thing!

Chapter 4: Basic Mash & Methods

ETHANOL PRODUCTION

4-1 This chapter deals with a most important aspect of distillation - producing the ethanol to be distilled. Through time and experience many good ways have evolved.

4-2 The process of fermentation has already been discussed. A little more is written on the subject in Chapter 6. Almost all of our beverage alcohol begins as fermentation, but fermentation alone will produce a drink no stronger than about 16 percent Ethanol (32 proof). In this chapter we shall learn a number of good ways to get reasonably close to that 32 proof beverage. Even 20 proof is reasonably close. In the next paragraphs we shall learn how to boost this proof as much as we might choose. By distillation, of course!

MASH RECIPES

4-3 You may be using any number of basic juices for fermenting your initial product for distillation. Whatever the nature of these we shall term them all as either Wort (pronounced wurt as in hurt) or Mash. It is still called Wort or Mash during fermentation. Mash is the popular usage, but Wort is more correct. After the Wort has fermented out fully we shall call it the Wash. Once it has been passed through a Still we shall call the portion left in the Still the Residue and the portion that passed through the still the **Distillate.**

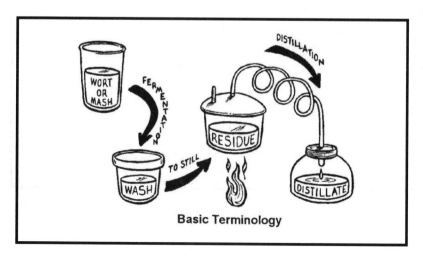

Basic Terminology

4-4 Washes can be produced from an infinite variety of different substances. The primary requirement is simply sugar in a dilute solution of water with a few nutrients (fertilizer, if you will), and vitamins. The nutrients needed are the usual nutrients for plant and animal life such as potassium, phosphates and a few trace elements. The B vitamins such as Thiamin and Riboflavin are helpful to furnish a healthy vigorous ferment. For a Thin Wort, as we shall call it, follow this recipe:

4-5 *NOTE:* unless otherwise indicated, all Wort recipes will be for one gallon of Wort. To make larger batches, simply multiply all of the ingredients (except for the yeast) by the number of gallons desired, and follow the same general instructions. In the case of the yeast its amount should only be increased slightly. For instance for a 5 gallon or 20 liter batch, use about a Tablespoon or 15 grams of yeast. The amount of yeast is not critical and greater amounts will not increase your yield. Greater amounts simply speed up the process by a small factor. Too TINY amount of yeast in a very LARGE wort may, however, be diluted to such a degree that it never grows and prospers.

THIN WORT MASH

Makes about One Gallon or 4 liters

2 lbs or .9 kilogram of sugar

1 level teaspoon baker's yeast or wine yeast (10 grams)

1 teaspoon vitamin-enriched yeast nutrient (10 grams)

1 Tablespoon of lemon juice or citric acid (15 grams)

1 Campden Tablet

Enough tepid (luke warm 75-90F/24-32C) water to make 1 gallon or 4 liters.

4-6 Yeast nutrient and Campden tablets can be purchased economically from a Home Winemaking Supplies Shop. Try to obtain vitamin enriched nutrient if possible. Dissolve the sugar, nutrient and lemon juice in enough water to make a total of 1 gallon or 4 liters. Stir extremely well and make a lot of bubbles in it. Oxygen from the air helps the yeast start to grow. Later on we want to exclude the oxygen. Add the yeast and cover with a loose fitting lid or cloth. DO NOT clamp down with a tight lid or you will be sorry! Much carbon dioxide gas is released as the fermentation proceeds and if you tightly cap it, the gas will generate enough pressure to burst your container and spread it evenly all over the room.

4-7 Keep the fermenting container in a warm room (75-80F/24-27C degrees). It should ferment vigorously within a few days and continue to ferment for one to two weeks. The fermentation will be visible as a bubbling, frothing, unsavory looking activity on top of the liquid. This is good. Don't complain if it doesn't fit your idea of an elegant mixture. It doesn't fit ours either, but it is necessary. Cheese, butter, yogurt, etc. all go through a similar
4-8 After a week or two, all activity should pretty much subside. Taste a tiny bit of the Wash (it won't hurt you). If it is sour, or at least unsweet, then the ferment is mostly over and you are ready to distill. If it is sweet, then it is not through fermenting and will need to set a while longer.

4-9 You can distill a Wash even if it does taste a little sweet, but it will not yield you quite as much alcohol as a totally fermented Wort. If it is only a little sweet, and you are not distilling any great amount, the difference isn't worth worrying about. Your yield will be very nearly the same. However, if you have a large batch, say a few hundred gallons, that slight sweetness is going to cost you a fair amount of pure alcohol, maybe a few gallons. Thus for small batches, you can afford to be a little inefficient, but not for large ones.

4-10 The above Wort is fine if you have lots of sugar available. Most people do not. Especially farmers. Thus, the usual Wort or Mash you have heard so much about doesn't resemble that described above. It is made from grain because grain is the commonest and cheapest raw material around. It also makes the smelliest Wort.

GRAIN WORT OR MASH

4-11 There are several basic steps in making a good grain wort. Each is important. It may seem complex at first - and it is - but once learned and mastered, it is an efficient Ethanol-producing system. The steps involved are Malting, Gristing, Mashing, Brewing, and Fermenting, in that order.

MALTING

4-12 Basically, malting converts the non-fermentable starch in a grain to fermentable sugar. Any grain such as corn, wheat, barley, rice, etc. or any combination of grains may be used. The grain used must be for seeding, because it must sprout before it is roasted. Here are a few hints on what to look for in a good malting grain:

> a) *It should have even grain size*
> b) *It should be fully ripe*
> c) *It should have "good condition" (i.e. sweet and dry)*
> d) *It should be internally floury...an indication of low nitrogen content.*
> e) *It should NOT BE chemically treated as many commercially sold seed grains are*

Choosing A Good Malting Barley	
A bushel should weigh About 56 pounds or 25 Kilos	**Moisture** - 15 percent
	Protein - 10 percent
	Fat - 2 percent
	Starch 50 percent
	Other - 23 percent

4-13 Soak the grain for 24 hours, change the water, and soak for another 24 hours. Skim off and discard anything that floats (husks, broken grains, contaminants, etc. The grain may be soaked a week without harm so it is best to leave it a little long. The grain grows best between 63-86F/17-30 C. It must not get too cold. When adding more water, the water should be cool but not cold.

4-14 Next, spread the drained seed out onto a wet surface (wet towels or clean burlap bags do nicely if not allowed to dry out). Keep it at room temperature (63-86F/17-30C) and wait - until it sprouts. Sprouting may take from a week to ten days. Wait until the sprout is about 1/4 inch or 6mm long. If the layer of grain is more than 1 inch or 2.5 cm deep,

1 thermometer **3**

After 3 or 4 days, very thin hair rootlets should be apparent.

Place soaked grain in heaps one to two feet high (30 to 60 cm). Leave for 12 to 24 hours. Internal temperature should not exceed 60F/16C degrees F.

2

1/2 to 2"

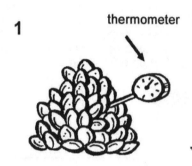

Spread grain evenly in a thin pile (in cool weather up to 2" or 5 cm deep in warm weather much less). Stir grain carefully every 5 or 6 hours to prevent heating up.

4

Once rootlets appear, start sprinkling lightly. Turn grain after sprinkling to spread water. USE WATER SPARINGLY. Use just enough to keep grain from drying out. Turn grain over after sprinkling and once or twice a day. Turn carefully to keep from tearing up rootlets. Keep temperature between 50-70F/10-21C.

or the grain is kept covered, it must be turned twice a day to ensure good ventilation.

4-15 Next, the newly-germinated seed must be dried out, preferably in a low temperature oven. When drying the malt, moderate the heat first. Do not let the temperature exceed 122F/50C until the malt appears to be dried. This will take a number of hours. Then raise the temperature

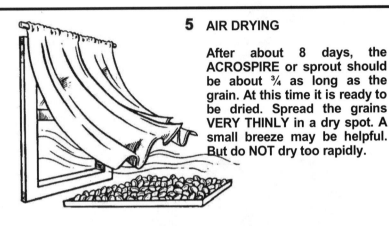

5   AIR DRYING

After about 8 days, the ACROSPIRE or sprout should be about ¾ as long as the grain. At this time it is ready to be dried. Spread the grains VERY THINLY in a dry spot. A small breeze may be helpful. But do NOT dry too rapidly.

6

KILN OR OVEN DRYING (4 day duration) - Turn malt once or twice each day. For PALE MALT, use this guide:

Day One	90-100F or 32-38C degrees
Day Two	100-120F or 38-49
Day Three	a.m.: 140F or 60C p.m.: 180F or 82C
Day Four	170F or 77C

For Ales, increase temperature slightly, but never exceed 220F/104C. Use of a mechanical turner will give best results.

slightly in 10F/5C degree steps but do not exceed 140F/60C degrees. Keep the temperature constant for an hour or so during each step. The grain is now Malted.

7. **CLEANING & DE-SPROUTING** - Rootlets are removed prior to gristing by placing the grain in a sack (such as a pillow case) and banging it repeatedly against some hard surface.

8. After knocking the rootlets loose, place the grain in a sieve and toss grains into the air to turn it over. The rootlets and chaff will fall through the holes in the sieve (best not done indoors).

9 GRISTING: Malt can be used now or stored for aging. Some brewers prefer to age the malt first for at least a few months. The malt is next gristed or broken up. Old coffee grinders with a coarse setting are excellent for this. A rolling pin can also be used, but is more work. If other grains are to be used in the wort, there are gristed along with the malt.

GRISTING

4-16 Now the grain is ready to be cracked or crushed to be made into grist. Cracking may be done in a coarse-grind grinder, a coffee grinder, or by using a rolling pin.

MASHING & BREWING

4-17 The next step is called mashing. This is where the rest of the Starch is converted to Sugar. Yeast can ferment only simple sugars - not starches. This conversion to sugar can be done in a number of ways. The simplest is boiling it for 45 minutes to an hour, then straining out the grain.

4-18 A much more efficient method, which allows the maximum extraction, is a longer process. Put 2LB/.9KG of grist (cracked or crushed malt) in a bucket of water with a glass immersion heater. Wrap the bucket in a blanket and let sit overnight or for 8 hours. 130-150F/54-66C degrees allows for maximum extraction. Strain liquid into a boiler and add enough water to make 3-4GAL/11-15LIT. Boil one hour. Test to see if starch has been converted completely by removing a teaspoon of wort and adding a little iodine to it. (Caution: Be sure to throw the mixture of malt and iodine away as iodine is Poisonous)! If the mixture turns blue, it has not yet all converted and may need further boiling.

4-19 When all the starch is converted (no color change - or very little color change -- when iodine added), the mixture is ready to use. The grain is now **Mashed.**

FERMENTING

4-20 After the wort or mash has cooled, to below 90F/32C, a tablespoon or two of yeast per gallon (4 liters) of Wort is added. If you have a small amount of yeast to start with then you can make a **YEAST STARTER** to extend out your yeast quantity to accommodate nearly ANY size batch.

4-21 Do this by mixing a few spoonfuls of your yeast into a sugary solution of orange juice. Mix enough sugar to make the juice very sweet but not sickeningly sweet. Make a cup or quart or liter or gallon, depending on the size of your mash batch. Leave this in a warm spot and it should be frothing merrily overnite. Leave it froth for a few days and it is ready to use.

4-22 The yeast or yeast starter will cause the wort to ferment. It is during this fermentation process that the sugar in the grain turns to Ethanol. Proper fermentation takes about 5 to 10 days. During this period, the temperature must be kept between 70-90F/21-32C. Skim off the foam during the first few days of fermentation.

POPULAR STRONG DRINKS

4-23 WHISKEY is produced from a grain wort or mash using the general method outlined in the last section. For different types of Whiskeys the formula and procedures are changed somewhat. We will list the changes in this section for the most popular Whiskey types.

4-24 For Bourbon Whiskey use 6 parts Corn, 2 parts Rye and 2 parts Barley. However, you malt Only the Barley. Then you make grist of all the grains (grind them together). Mix them and proceed into your mashing and brewing in the normal way. In the next section we will explain why it is not necessary to malt all of the constituents.

4-25 Sour Mash Whiskey follows the normal recipe, but requires that you add the dregs from a previous batch to your new wort in place of the yeast, and let the fermentation proceed naturally from the dormant yeast cells in these dregs. You do not add any new yeast to your Sour Mash. Of course, you cannot make Sour Mash Whiskey until you have made at least one batch of Sweet Whiskey since you will not have the dregs until then. The name stems from the fact that, normally, the old dregs taste and smell a little sour because they are slightly acid.

4-26 Sweet Mash Whiskey, as its name implies, uses new yeast.

4-27 For **Pure Rye Whiskey**, only Rye is malted, gristed and mashed. Most recipes, however, use about 9 parts of Rye grain and add 1 part Malted Barley (the Rye is NOT malted in this case...It is ground to a grist with the Barley Malt and mashed in the usual way).

4-28 Irish Whiskey uses 10 parts of malted barley, 7 parts of fresh barley grain, and 1 part each of fresh oats, rye and wheat grains. Thus half of the grist is malted grain and half is fresh grain. The grist is mashed and brewed in the normal manner.

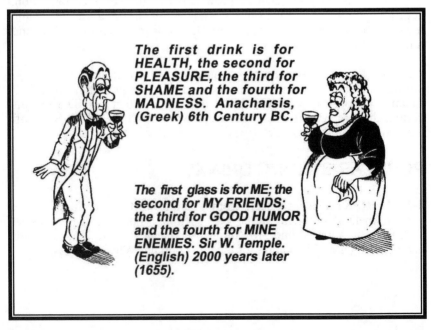

The first drink is for HEALTH, the second for PLEASURE, the third for SHAME and the fourth for MADNESS. Anacharsis, (Greek) 6th Century BC.

The first glass is for ME; the second for MY FRIENDS; the third for GOOD HUMOR and the fourth for MINE ENEMIES. Sir W. Temple. (English) 2000 years later (1655).

4-29 Scotch Whiskeys derive their very thin claim to fame primarily because their malt is dried by smoking it with Peat smoke and they use local water in their washes. If you wish to believe that this somehow imparts them with expensive unique characteristics you may, of course, do so. The distillers of some of these products spend much money trying to create this illusion.

4-30 For **Rum** use the Thin Wort recipe on page 44, but substitute molasses for the sugar. You will have to use a Wine Hydrometer to adjust the Specific Gravity of the Wort to about 1.060 to 1.070. Then ferment in the normal way to obtain the Wash.

4-31 Vodka is little more than a mixture of Ethanol and water. Use the thin wort recipe given previously and distill it to a very high proof. This removes almost all of the Congenerics (minute quantities of chemical byproducts that enter greatly into the aging process, and impart much of the flavor and "character" to the beverage) and leaves very nearly a pure alcohol (180 proof or so). Then cut this down with pure water to the proof level desired using Chart A in Chapter 12.

4-32 Gins are heavily rectified (remember that word?) as is Vodka. The usual wort consists of 16 parts corn grain, 3 parts Malt, and 1 part Rye grain. However, just before the last rectification a little flavoring, such as Juniper Berry is added to the Wash which replaces the natural Congenerics with the artificial side products of the additive. Other additives are Licorice, Angelica, Almonds, and sugar (2 to 5 percent). The resulting very Ethanolic drink (120 proof or more) is then cut down to the desired proof level. Dry Gin is distilled out to a higher proof level before cutting it back down with water. Hence the name "Dry".

4-33 Brandy is usually the result of only one or at most two simple distillations. Also the wash used is a "new" wine (not aged) of one type or another. For true Brandy, grapes are used. This grape wine is then distilled and the distillate is simply called Brandy. For all other fruits and vegetables, a new wine of the appropriate type is used. For instance, Apricot Wine is used to make Apricot Brandy. Carrot Wine to make Carrot Brandy etc. For anything other than Brandy made from grapes the wine type is appended to the name as illustrated above.

AGING

4-34 Almost all liquors are aged, with the possible exceptions of Vodkas and Gins. Previously used Oak barrels are considered the best if kept sweet and clean. If none are available charred oak casks are used. These barrels allow the liquor to "breathe" through its pores. The minute amounts of air thus introduced alter the congenerics (Esters and Aldehydes primarily) which undergo very slow but very definite chemical transformations during the "aging" process.

4-35 Oak barrels supply small amounts of tannin. The charcoaled barrel sides provide some filtering action and gravity induces some settling. The Ethanol content actually decreases a little. Three or four years is probably the average aging time for most liquors. Some even do well up to 10 or 20 years. Fine Napoleon Brandies over 75 years old are - as one source exclaims in despair - "a bit of romantic nonsense". Liquor does not automatically get better with age. After a certain point it gets worse.. and worse! Any liquor, wine or beer over 25 years old should be suspect.

MALTING & MASHING EXPLAINED

4-36 A while back we quickly went through the process of making a wort or mash from grains. If we did our job correctly, you should have understood the fermenting and the gristing. If you did your job correctly, you should be wondering about the malting and mashing. What is all this hocus-pocus about sprouting the grains, drying them and then boiling it all to a pulp? You don't really have to understand the process to make it work but if something goes wrong it is easier to correct if you understand the process.

4-37 Enzymes are really the name of the game from here on in. They occur everywhere in life processes. You have them in your mouth, your stomach and your intestines to name just a few places. They are not completely understood even by scientists. They are proteins like gelatin or steak. They do not enter into any active combinations themselves; therefore their action is usually termed Catalytic. They aid the body in breaking down its food supply so that it can extract the energy and building blocks it needs. Not only our bodies, but any living bodies - including yeasts!

4-38 Now we come to the crux of the matter. Yeast can only utilize very simple sugars for a food supply. Most products in nature are composed of starches, cellulose, complex sugars, and other unsavory materials that yeast cannot use. But Enzymes can trigger the breaking down of many of these other materials into simple sugars. For instance the enzyme Ptyallin in your mouth starts breaking down starches into sugar before the food even gets into your stomach.

4-39 Three Important Facts: First, Enzymes are proteins (such as steak or gelatin) and therefore extremes of heat for any length of time) for instance boiling water) will destroy their effectiveness. Secondly, only a small concentration of enzymes is necessary to cause a complete chemical transformation. A single enzyme can aid the transformation of several thousands of chemical reactions (such as sugar to alcohol) in a single minute. Thirdly, enzymes are very specialized. Although 10 or 20 different enzymes acting independently can cause a very complex reaction, each one is very specialized and can do only a single, very simple, step. And it can only do that same simple step over...and over....and over....and over.

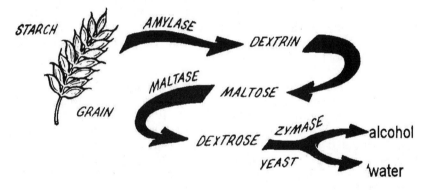

4-40 Grains are primarily starch. However, they contain a group of Enzymes called **Amylases**, one of which will help reduce the starch to **Dextrin** (a gummy adhesive used for sizing) and another of the Amylases, an enzyme call **Diastase**, will further act on the dextrin to help reduce it to the sugar **Maltose**. Another enzyme present **Maltase**, helps convert Maltose to **Dextrose**...a very simple sugar. These enzymes (Amylase, Diastase, Maltase) are natural constituents of grains and some other starchy food products. They normally exist in too short supply to act as catalysts. When a grain sprouts, however, these enzymes multiply enormously to help convert the starchy part of the grain into sugars so the young grain plant can utilize the sugar for food.

AFTER DRYING IN OVEN   **AFTER GRISTING**

4-41 We take advantage of this fact and wet the grain down in a warm place. This "tricks" the grain's internal chemistry into thinking that spring has arrived, and it starts to sprout which greatly increases the Enzymes *(Germination)*. If we let this process continue for any length of time, the sprout would soon eat up the food supply and our whole purpose would be defeated. So we let it sprout long enough for the Enzymes to multiply and start the conversion but not long enough for the food supply to be used up in the growing process. This occurs when the sprouts are about 1/4 inch or .6 CM long.

4-42 At this point we terminate the process by drying the grain out at a moderate oven temperature of 120F/49C or so. This introduces what would be extreme drought conditions on the grain and the sprout dies and withers away. We are left with the enzyme, some starch, some dextrin, some malt and some dextrose (and the hulls, too, of course). The temperature is just high enough to stop the growing process and yet low enough to avoid harming the enzymes. The resulting product is now called **Malt**.

AFTER DRYING IN OVEN   **AFTER GRISTING**

4-43 Our next step is to set up the ideal conditions for the enzymes to finish their job of conversion of the *Malt* into *Dextrose*. The grain is converted to Grist and immersed in water in order to allow the enzymes and grains to circulate freely and come into maximum contact. The *Diastase* and *Maltase* enzymes convert more rapidly at moderately high temperatures and after adding the temperature is usually anywhere from 130-150F/54-66C. Some reliable sources recommend 154F/68C degrees as the ideal "conversion" temperature.

4-44 After the conversion to Dextrose, the temperature is reduced because the yeasts-which are added in the next step-are very much more sensitive to extremes of temperature than are enzymes. More water is added to the mash, if needed, after it has cooled. Then yeast is added after it has cooled down to 90F/32C or less. The yeasts produce their own enzyme, Zymase, which converts the Dextrose to Alcohol and water. It is a long chain. Each step of the way is paved with an enzyme performing its single function.

4-45 It should be clear as to why a good many recipes call for only a small percentage of the total grist to be malted. A relatively small amount of enzymes will perform an enormous amount of conversions. At elevated temperatures (so long as they are not too high) the conversions take place even more quickly. Obviously, the smaller the percentage of the malt present in a mash the longer you are going to need to brew it.

PREPARATION OF WASHES FOR DISTILLATION

4-46 The Wash cannot simply be dumped into the still for distilling. All washes will have a fair number of impurities in them and grain washes, especially, may be saturated to the point of being soupy. If this mixture were put into the still you would soon clog it up. The wash should either be siphoned or carefully poured off the dregs (bottom sediment) as a first step in cleansing. Always be careful from this point onward not to aerate your products any more than necessary. Undesired byproducts will be formed if you keep stirring in more oxygen and other air-borne material. This is directly opposite to the procedure given before the yeasts were added, at which time you intentionally stirred in air to help with ferment.

4-47 After the dregs have been discarded, the wash can be left to set for a few hours or even days for further settling. Usually it is clear enough to be distillable if it is carefully siphoned once again. The cleaner the wash material is kept, the easier the still will be to operate. And the longer between cleanings!

FREEZE DISTILLATION

4-48 The common home freezer can be used to effect a fair distillation. The Wash is kept in the freezer until it turns mushy. It can then be poured or ladled into a large strainer cloth and squeezed dry. The liquid squeezing out will be higher in alcoholic content than the frozen residue left in the strainer cloth. This method works well enough to make "fortified" wines (20 to 30 percent alcohol) out of ordinary wines. The temperature of the freezer, length of time frozen, and techniques used to reclaim the Ethanol all enter into determining how efficient the process will be. Up north in the lands of Alaska, Minnesota, Montana, Alberta, Saskatchewan and, especially, the Northwest Territories, the great outdoors can be used as a crude still during the cold winter months.

Chapter 5: Still Hardware

There once was a man, Bill, with a still

That Bill built on the top of a hill.

When he started the fire,

The hill burned entire

And they billed Bill

for the Hill

and the Still.

5-1 This chapter is approximately in the center of the book. Since it is the heart of the book its placement is appropriate. In this chapter we show and explain the hardware that is used for DISTILLATION. There are many degrees of sophistication in this equipment. We will touch upon all of the major types of stills and cover in greater detail those stills that are practical to build for small and medium size outputs. These latter stills use, in general, materials and components that can be easily obtained in any civilized country.

SINGLE-STAGE STILLS

5-2 Figure 1 shows a basic **Retort Still** diagram. This is the simplest still possible. From it we can define the terms used in distilling and then move on to more practical models. A **Retort** is simply a glass flask, or bulb, with an elongated tube built into the top. It is designed for distillation on a very small scale in laboratories.

5-3 The Still itself consists of the so-called hardware (in this case glassware) in its entirety. In Figure 1 the letter A denotes the evaporating vessel and its provisions for heating. The **Wash** is denoted by B (called the **Residue** after the distillation is completed), the **Vapor** by

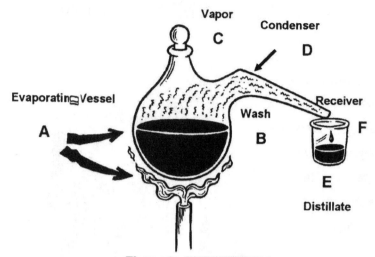

Figure 1: RETORT STILL

C, the **Condenser** by D, the **Receiver** by F and the **Distillate** (or **Condensate**) by E. For this simple example it is easy to fix these terms in mind because each step is so obvious.
However they apply to any and all stills and distilling apparatus no matter how complex or simple.

5-4 The trouble with the simple retort still is that it is inefficient and slow and the retort cannot handle large quantities. It cannot cool the vapor fast enough. It's no problem vaporizing as you need only apply more and more heat. But to condense, you need to cool the vapor down to condensing temperatures (the temperature at which vapor turns to liquid). This temperature depends on the liquids involved, the pressure and the humidity. If you are only barely vaporizing the liquid, then it is easier to condense it all, as only a small amount of heat must be removed from the vapor to accomplish this, But such a process would be incredibly slow.

5-5 We can improve this Simple Retort Still by making the condenser more efficient as shown in Figure 2. The condenser tube is lengthened and an enclosed water jacket is put around it. Cool water is then forced through the jacket from the bottom inlet upward. This keeps the coolest part of the jacket at all times toward the condensate or distillate end and, hence, increases the yield. This improvement (in laboratory models) came just prior to the Civil War, and is credited to Justus van Liebig.

The credit turns out to be evidently misplaced. However it is called the **Liebig Condenser** to this day.

5-6 Another deficiency of the simple retort still design was the lack of any device to indicate when the Ethanol was going, going, gone. If you don't shut the still off at the right time, it simply undoes its good work and adds more and more WATER to the Ethanol that has been distilled off. Because of the rather drastic change in temperature occurring when the last of the ethanol has boiled off, a thermometer is always used in the evaporating vessel or in the vapor, and referred to constantly as the distillation proceeds. Figure 2 shows these basic improvements.

5-7 Another difficulty encountered and solved was the tendency of a simple still to be "sloppy" in its work. As is well known, water **DOES** evaporate without any external heat supply. Obviously, it evaporates

---

Figure 2: ADDITION OF LIEBIG CONDENSER & THERMOMETER

Used for laboratory work in distillation. Although not practical for large scale production, such stills are of much use in explaining and understanding the principles involved.

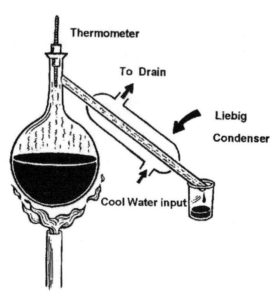

even faster when heated. So while the Ethanol is BOILING off, a fair amount of water is EVAPORATING off at the same time, resulting in a MIXTURE of Ethanol and water in the distillate. In Chapter 3 we mentioned that a mixture of liquids in a simple still resulted in a rather imperfect first separation. It is true that much more Ethanol than water ends up in the distillate, but it is also true that a lot of water makes it over the hump. In Chapter 3 we also mentioned that the only cure for this in a simple still is to run the distillate through the still again--and perhaps again and again. Each time it will become purer Ethanol until the solution becomes Azeotropic at a concentration of 97.2 percent Ethanol by volume. Does this sound vaguely familiar? If not it will soon get that way as we continue probing and exploring.

5-8 In the next section we will discuss these latest deficiencies. Other noteworthy improvements for simple stills are 1) the addition of a safety valve, and 2) enclosing the system entirely so that no distillate can evaporate into the atmosphere. A safety valve can be easily added by drilling a hole in the top of the evaporating vessel then plugging the hole with a heavy, round marble (slightly larger than the hole).

5-9 You will note at this point that we are using examples of Ethanol (Ethyl Alcohol) and water because that is what this book is all about. However, all of this is equally applicable to any solution capable of being separated by distillation. Even solutions of dozens of different liquids, as we shall see later on.

5-10 In a simple still, the first portion of the distillate to condense is called the Heads and it is the purest. The last portion to come over is called the Tails and it is the most dilute and most likely to contain any contaminants present such as Esters, higher alcohols, etc.

5-11 Since we will be discussing proofs to some extent from this point onward, it will do to mention that in the United States a Proof Gallon of liquor contains 50 percent Ethanol by volume (NOT 100 percent as is sometimes believed). All tax rates are given in terms of Proof Gallon and liquors containing more or less than 50 percent are taxed on the percentage that they do contain--which is a fair system since it is only the Ethanol that is taxed.

COMPOUND STILLS

5-12 Most of the stills and innovations discussed up to this point are useful only on a laboratory scale. The simple pot still (to be discussed later) produces only a small fraction of the total liquor in the United

States, Great Britain and Canada. Compound Stills have a greater degree of sophistication built into them and are faster, cheaper and simpler to operate. The Compound Still is practical on either the laboratory or commercial level. Thousands of different types have been built and tried by engineers, moonshiners, and bootleggers alike. In this section we will cover primarily those designed by the engineers. In the final section we will offer some versions cooked up by various moonshiners and pot boilers over the years. More than one moonshiner could very well have qualified for a degree in engineering!

REFLUX STILL

5-13 Figure 3 is a simple, but quite workable, **Reflux Still**. It is a classical type built by professionals and amateurs alike. It is an excellent type for illustrating basic principles. Probably more variations of this type have been built than all other types combined. As you will notice there is no radical departure from what we have discussed here-to-fore except for the **Reflux Tower** or **Reflux Comum** on top of the still. The Wash container is fitted with a gas fueled firebox to operate from natural gas or propane. This makes it easy to adjust the heat input to close tolerances. The **Wash box** needs to be stainless steel or some other equally inert material as the hot wash increases the activity of the acids. Copper is also used but needs to be kept very clean between uses to avoid corrosion and, hence, contamination and fouling of the Wash.

5-14 The Reflux Column is mounted on top of the Wash box and welded or bolted securely to it. A stainless steel disc, perforated with many small holes, is all that separates the Wash Box from the inside of the Reflux Column. The Reflux Column is filled with large round balls of a non-porous, non-active material such as ordinary marbles. Obviously the holes in the perforated steel disc must be smaller than the marble diameters or the marbles will simply fall through into the Wash Box and stop the whole operation. Sometimes such things as wire helices and-or Stainless Steel Wool are used in the Reflux Column in place of the marbles. Many other items will work, but they must be made of a material that is relatively inert to mild acids so they will not foul the distillate.

5-15 The operation of the Reflux Column is disarmingly simple. Since water vapor travels with the lower-boiling Ethanol into the distillate, a simple way to prevent the water vapor from making it
over all the way is to start cooling the vapors *JUST A LITTLE BIT*

Figure 3: REFLUX STILL

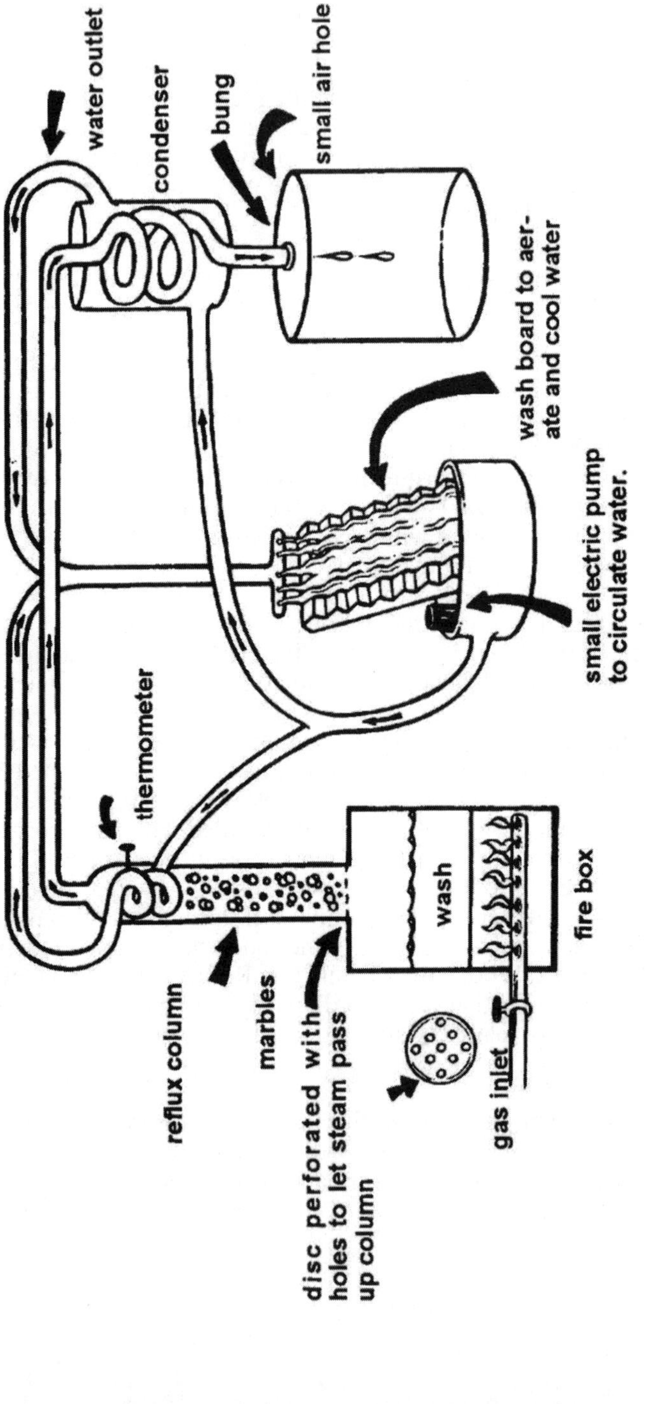

water outlet

condenser

bung

small air hole

wash board to aer-
ate and cool water

small electric pump
to circulate water.

thermometer

fire box

wash

gas inlet

marbles

reflux column

disc perforated with
holes to let steam pass
up column

before they travel over into the condenser. With much cooling ALL the vapors will tend to start condensing back into the liquid state and fall back down in the reflux tower. However, by providing only a tiny bit of cooling the component that is going to condense first is going to be the one that has the highest boiling point; water, in this case. The marbles provide a small degree of isolation from the heat and a little condensation of the water starts to take place. The marbles also provide a large surface area on which the condensation can occur. Naturally the coolest marbles are at the top and most condensation will occur there, and, under the influence of gravity, start dropping downward back into the Wash Box.

5-16 Of course, some Ethanol also condenses out on the cooler top marbles but as the liquid descends, and the marbles become warmer and warmer, the Ethanol will tend to evaporate first and go back into vapor and proceed upward again. Inverse or Reflux action takes place. The vapor traveling upward tends to become purer Ethanol. The vapor traveling downward tends to become purer water. It actually becomes a two-way distilling system. *A SINGLE RUN THROUGH A GOOD REFLUX STILL WILL USUALLY BE WORTH THREE OR FOUR RUNS THROUGH A COMMON POT STILL.* This will give you an idea of the enormous efficiency afforded by a reflux still design. A typical single run through a pot still may yield a distillate containing 20 to 30 percent Ethanol from a wash which contained perhaps 10 percent Ethanol. A single run through a reflux still of fair design can yield a distillate in excess of 90 percent (180 proof) from the same wash!

5-17 Some other improvements are afforded by the design in Figure 3. The condenser is an elaborate version of the Liebig condenser with many, many coils of stainless steel or copper tubing wrapped tightly inside a water tight tank. The receiving barrel needs no comment other than to say it should be appropriate for a food product: plastic lined, wood or stainless steel. In order to avoid throwing away an enormous amount of water --in the best of ecological tradition-- a recycling operation is set up. A small electric pump operated from a battery or house current pumps water through the water jacket on the Liebig condenser. In order to help cool the water, a corrugated wash board (hard to find these anymore!) is set up inside the tub and the return water is allowed to flow over these ribs in open air on its way down to the tub. Some of the liquid evaporates in so doing, and this in turn cools the remaining liquid. Of course, because some water evaporates on a continuing basis it will have to be replenished from time to time; but not nearly so much nor nearly so often as if the water was simply thrown away.

FIGURE 4: ENLARGEMENT OF TYPICAL REFLUX TOWER SHOWN IN FIGURE 3

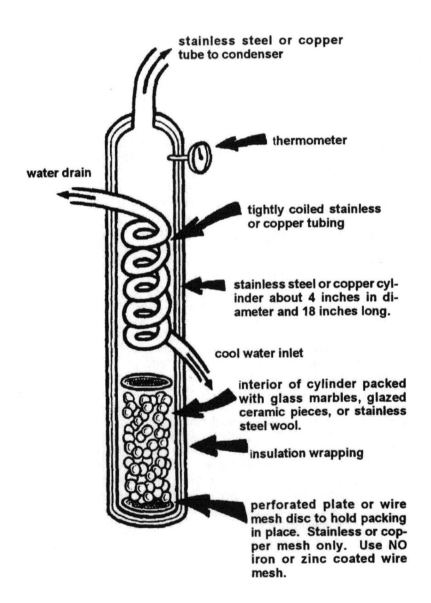

stainless steel or copper tube to condenser

thermometer

water drain

tightly coiled stainless or copper tubing

stainless steel or copper cylinder about 4 inches in diameter and 18 inches long.

cool water inlet

interior of cylinder packed with glass marbles, glazed ceramic pieces, or stainless steel wool.

insulation wrapping

perforated plate or wire mesh disc to hold packing in place. Stainless or copper mesh only. Use NO iron or zinc coated wire mesh.

5-18 If there is a creek or stream nearby this tub affair is not necessary. The water can be pumped or channeled from upstream and ejected a little ways downstream. Unless some gigantic operation is underway, this will not heat the water to any measurable extent even a few feet downstream--it won't upset any ecological balances. It also will in no way contaminate the water.

FRACTIONAL DISTILLATION

5-19 Fractional Distillations has little to do with the efficient construction of Stills for Ethanol. However this is an excellent opportunity to see how other fields use Distillation Techniques--in this case the oil industry.

5-20 Fractional Distillations takes place in a Reflux still put to very sophisticated use. Recall it was mentioned previously that a still not only can separate two components mixed together but even dozens. One very good use for such a still is the separation of crude oil into all of its basic components. Crude oil contains such things as Propane, Butane, Octane, etc. all of which have different boiling points. Of course we know them better as Gasoline, Naphtha, Kerosene, Fuel Oil, Lubricating Oil, Grease, Paraffin, and just plain old tar. But they are all contained in crude oil and need to be extracted to keep the industrial revolution from becoming an insurrection.

5-21 Figure 5 shows a sophisticated reflux fractionating column. Of course, you realize that highly paid engineers are not going to use anything so simple as marbles in their columns. This column uses a very popular and efficient method known as the Bubble Plate Volume. The principle is the same, however. The rising vapor Bubbles through the liquid and around the plates on its way upward and passes through several consecutive vaporization and condensations. The liquid flows down through the tubes. At various points on the column the level of volatility will be correspondingly different and a hole cut through the surrounding jacket at that point will release all those vapors falling within a certain range. Notice that this is a Continuous still in that the feed point is above the bottom of the still. Thus it works downward also in an inverse manner and the materials Denser than the average of those coming in, such as pitch and tar, exit through lower portions of the column. Many commercial Ethanol stills are also of this continuous action design.

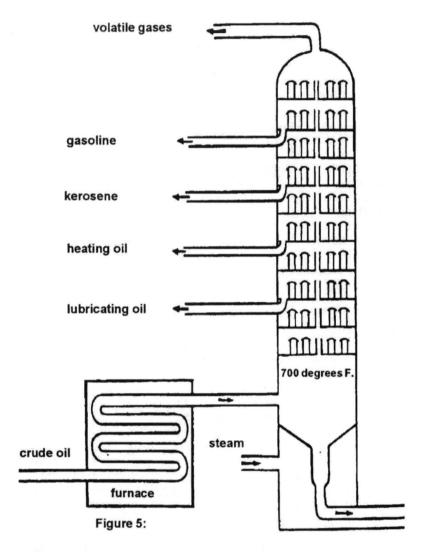

volatile gases

gasoline

kerosene

heating oil

lubricating oil

700 degrees F.

crude oil

steam

furnace

Figure 5:

MODERN, CONTINOUS RUN FRACTIONATING COLUMN FOR SEPARATING MANY DIFFERENT COMPONENTS SUCH AS CRUDE OIL AS PICTURED HERE.

Residue containing tar, pitch, paraffin, etc.

HOME MADE STILLS

5-22 More stills have been built by the home enthusiast throughout history than there probably are people. That would make over 4 billion to date which seems like a reasonable number. Most of these were useless and many blew up taking their lackluster designers with them. But some were successful and a few even brought forth technological innovations of historic proportions.

5-23 We have gathered together a few of the popular ones in this section. If you concentrated reasonably well while reading the preceding sections and chapters these models will need only a little further explanation as to their workings. Some notes are added where it is thought necessary to explain unusual features.

POT STILL OPERATIONS (refer to Figure 6)

5-24 If the mash is very soupy, do not fill these pots too full, or they will clog the condenser lines with mash solids. After heat is applied, the first distillate starts dripping into the receiver at 170-180F/77-82C degrees. Any distillates coming over before 170F/77C should be discarded (it may contain small amounts of Methyl alcohol and other impurities). Keep the heat moderate. Within an hour or two, more or less, the temperature should gradually rise to 205F/96F degrees. The heat is removed at this point and the distillate should be about 40 to 60 percent Ethanol. This is a very good yield for a pot still in one run. The rise in temperature is critical--watch for it closely. The times given can vary widely depending on the size and throughput of the device. For a very tiny mash sample the whole process might be over in 15 minutes.

5-25 Remember too, the temperatures and times given here are for sea level. These will be good enough values for altitudes up to a thousand or even two thousand feet. Above this height the boiling points will decrease enough to be noticeable and some minor adjustments will need to be made to your times and temperatures. Most of humanity resides within that comfortable range in altitude so this is not normally a bothersome consideration. Ambient (or outside) temperature can also affect your timing. For instance a large outdoors still close to the Arctic Circle will vary a little in its operational time and temperatures from those given here.

5-26 Discard the residue and clean out the entire still and tubing after each and every run. If purer Ethanol is desired, repeat the operation exactly as above to get a yield of about 70 percent

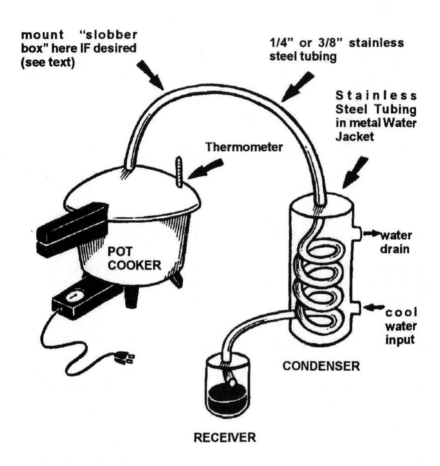

mount "slobber box" here IF desired (see text)

1/4" or 3/8" stainless steel tubing

Stainless Steel Tubing in metal Water Jacket

Thermometer

POT COOKER

water drain

cool water input

CONDENSER

RECEIVER

Figure 6:
EFFICIENT HOME POT STILL (Model A)
"Work horse of the ages"

Ethanol. Remember that the slower you distill the purer the product. Also remember that it is quite flammable from this point onward. *NEVER LET THE TEMPERATURE EXCEED 210F/99C OR THE BOILING POINT, WHICHEVER IS LOWER. Watch it constantly!!*

5-27 If the highest possible percentage of Ethanol is desired from each run then more care needs to be exercised. The heat should be applied carefully (slower) since the action is rapid. Stop the still action at 180F/82C instead of the usual 205F/96C. This can increase the yield to near 85 percent Ethanol. A third and fourth run following these same instructions, will yield Ethanol of 90 to 95 percent.

SLOBBER BOXES

5-28 Although this name is indelicate it is one of the common descriptive pieces of jargon invented by some unknown moonshiner. A slobber box can assume many different configurations but the one shown in Figure 7 is representative. Essentially, it can be a tin can or aluminum can, square or round, with an inlet and an outlet as shown. This is mounted in the line between the cooker and the condenser. It allows most of the impurities that follow the Ethanol across to have a "drop-off point" ahead of the condenser and receiver. This gives a much cleaner distillate. In practice it is simply an enlarged portion of the tubing where solids particulate matter, water vapor, etc. can re-condense or drop out. The small hose leading out of the bottom of the slobber box can be used to drain it periodically to keep the pathway clear.

5-29 The use of a Slobber Box is not mandatory but it is desirable when a reflux tower is not used. When a reflux tower is used the tower, itself, performs this same function. If a slobber box is not used then a larger part of the FIRST part of the distillate coming through should be discarded. For a six or eight quart pot cooker without a slobber box it is advisable to set aside the first few ounces (50 to 100 grams) coming through. Since this is bound to be very rich in Ethanol it can be saved and added to a later batch to be redistilled. With a slobber box only a tablespoon or two (20 grams or less than an ounce) of the first distillate through needs to be discarded.

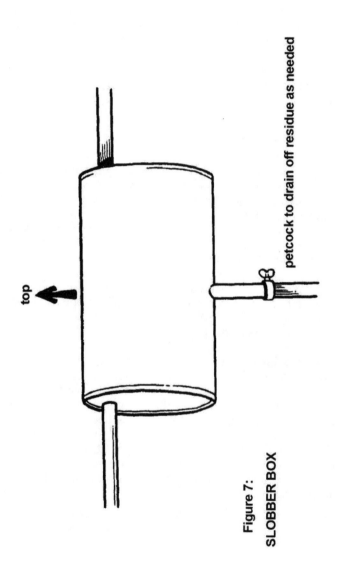

top

petcock to drain off residue as needed

Figure 7:
SLOBBER BOX

THE CONNELLY ICE WATER STILL

5-30 Here is the ideal still for the entrepreneur living at the corner of Constitution & Pennsylvania Avenue in Washington D.C. (The IRS is two blocks away, the Dept of Justice is the same, and the U.S. Court House is right across the street). This is a pretty tricky place to live so the still had better NOT look anything LIKE a still.

5-31 The only items needed are some carefully proportioned pans and a few feet of half-inch copper plumbing pipes or glass rods. Figure 8 shows the details of construction. The large basin on the top should have a rounded bottom so that the escaping vapor condensing on it will roll to the bottom and drop into the small bowl or cup. The small bowl is suspended in the middle of a tripod made from three carefully measured copper pipes or glass rods. If the size of the three containers is carefully chosen to fit just right a fantastically simple still can be built that is moderately efficient. Ice cubes from the refrigerator can be used in the top pan. All of the still parts can double for normal kitchen use, making this design economical for the crimped budget.

5-32 Although this is a charming and deceivingly simple still it is not nearly so efficient as other designs. To increase its efficiency somewhat, keep the heat as low as possible. This will allow more of the alcohol to condense before it is lost as an escaping vapor.

HOME POT STILL (Model B)

5-33 This still is very similar in construction to the **Model B, HOME POT STILL.** As with the Model A, the pot cooker is usually a converted pressure cooker which can be electric or a stove-top variety. The heat should be easily adjustable so that it can be turned low as soon as the temperature on the thermometer reaches the area of 170F/77C. The tubing leading from the cooker can be flexible plastic or a rubber type that is sold as "food-grade" material. If properly chosen it will fit tightly over the center outlet on the cooker where the pressure weight usually sits (such as on some Presto Model cookers) and requires NO modification of the cooker lid.

5-34 There is a small rubber grommet on many lids that contains a little metal pivot which is used as the safety valve. If the grommet is left intact but the metal pivot removed, a thin thermometer will fit through the grommet snugly. If it fits too tightly get a thinner thermometer or try a different grommet. It needs to be a snug fit but easily movable up and

Figure 8:
THE CONNELLY ICE-WATER STILL

porcelain or stainless steel wash basin or llarge pan that fits moderately snug, but with ample room for steam to escape

crushed ice or ice-cubes

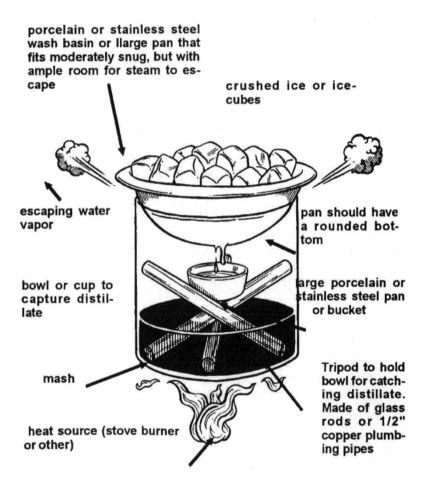

escaping water vapor

pan should have a rounded bottom

bowl or cup to capture distillate

arge porcelain or stainless steel pan or bucket

mash

heat source (stove burner or other)

Tripod to hold bowl for catching distillate. Made of glass rods or 1/2" copper plumbing pipes down. Again no modification of the lid is needed and the safety valve can be put back together again. Never forget, however, that the thermometer is now the safety valve also. If too much pressure is allowed the thermometer will be blown out of the lid so keep this in mind and always be sure that the generated steam can be heard hissing through your pipes into the slobber box and condenser radiator.

5-35 An economical pressure gauge can be purchased at a hardware and mounted on the lid. Some pressure cookers come with their own gauges. The pressure should remain close to zero. After all you are using the container NOT as a pressure cooker but as a SEALED container with ONE free outlet. If you could seal the EDGES of any other pan or container it would work just as well. Many other pans or containers with removable lids can be improvised to do the same job just as efficiently. NEVER, however, use or improvise anything that is totally sealed or can inadvertently become totally sealed. There must always be a good clear exit for the vapors and the exit must never be so tiny that excessive pressures can build up behind it.

5-36 The thermometer will always give you prior warning if you are prudent. A higher pressure in the cooker is going to cause the temperature to rise also. So if you get a sudden and rapid increase in temperature shut down the operation and check for plugged lines (after the pressure and temperature drop to low values--temperatures below 150F/66C). *IN NO EVENT SHOULD YOU ALLOW THE TEMPERATURE TO EXCEED 210F/99C. Watch it constantly!*

5-37 The slobber box is constructed and operates exactly as described previously.

5-38 The biggest real difference in the operation of this still is the very efficient and easy-to-operate air conditioner radiator. These radiators normally are constructed entirely of copper tubing and you should check for this before using it. No lead solder is used in their construction so they are safe from any obvious problems of metal poisoning. The radiator should be clean and should be flushed before usage with hot soapy water (with degreaser added) and then with boiling hot clear water. If done thoroughly this will get rid of any oils or greases and other soluble contaminants that might have settled there. After the still is first set up the pot cooker should be filled with pure water and this should ALL be boiled and run through the tubing and condenser into the distillate collector. This should pretty well finish cleaning up the entire apparatus.

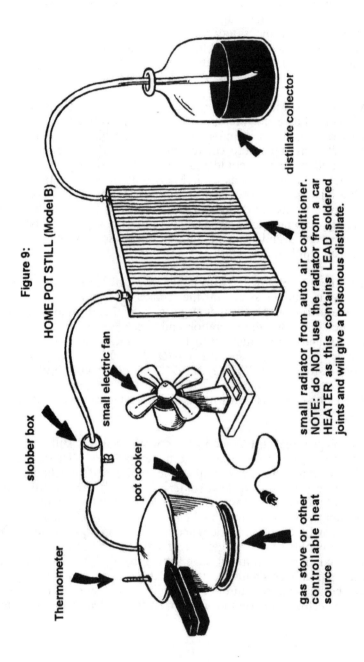

Figure 9:

HOME POT STILL (Model B)

distillate collector

small radiator from auto air conditioner.
NOTE: do NOT use the radiator from a car
HEATER as this contains LEAD soldered
joints and will give a poisonous distillate.

slobber box

small electric fan

Thermometer

pot cooker

gas stove or other
controllable heat
source

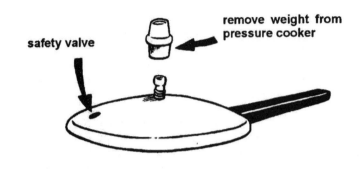

safety valve

remove weight from
pressure cooker

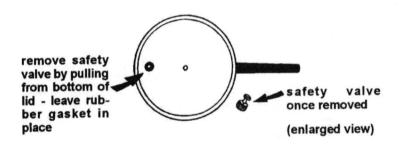

remove safety
valve by pulling
from bottom of
lid - leave rub-
ber gasket in
place

safety valve
once removed

(enlarged view)

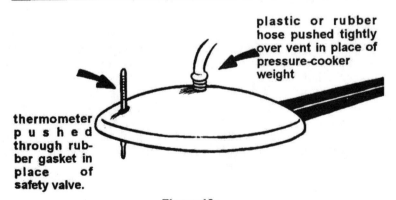

plastic or rubber
hose pushed tightly
over vent in place of
pressure-cooker
weight

thermometer
p u s h e d
through rub-
ber gasket in
place of
safety valve.

Figure 10:

CONVERTING A PRESSURE COOKER LID FOR USE AS A STILL

Then drain everything, clean it up, and start the first batch of mash or wash through the still.

5-39 In operation you need a small electric fan to adjust the operation of the condenser. The fan performs the same function as the running water does in the normal water-cooled condenser. Remember, however, that the normal air conditioner radiator is very, very efficient and it will not take too much air current to keep it running plenty cool. If you use too much air the radiator will run too cool and the radiator will act as the distillate collector and it will all condense there. On the other hand, if you don't have enough air circulation the radiator will run too hot and steam will come out of the tube leading into the distillate collector. Which means you will be losing a good deal of your Ethanol vapor into the air.

5-40 Since most fans do not have a multitude of different speeds the air control can be controlled more closely and evenly by using a cardboard or similar deflector. Put a piece of cardboard over the half of the radiator toward the collector bottle (thereby blocking the air from the fan on that half). Thus most of your cooling will be directed over the uncovered half of the radiator closest to the pot cooker. A little playing around with the cardboard will allow you to find the optimum position for the fan and the cardboard. You can control its operation very closely with this simple device. Aside from these small differences in construction and operation the still should operate in the same manner as the Model **A POT COOKER STILL** and the same general instructions and admonitions apply.

CONTINUOUS RUN STILL

5-41 This still is a very simplified Continuous Run Still. The wash needs to be well strained or made from a Thin Wash Recipe, as any particles will gum up the works. Briefly, the wash travels down the siphon tube and strikes the hot bottom plate of the soldering iron (heat source). This vaporizes most of the Ethanol which bubbles up through the small amount of water in the bottom of the soldering iron, and enters the tiny reflux tower on its way to the receiver. The water that precipitates from the reflux column joins the water already present in the bottom of the soldering iron and exits through the drain tube located about an inch above the top of the soldering iron head.

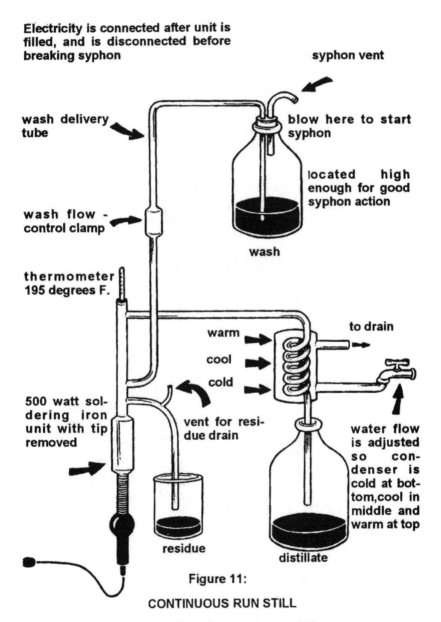

Electricity is connected after unit is filled, and is disconnected before breaking syphon

syphon vent

wash delivery tube

blow here to start syphon

located high enough for good syphon action

wash flow - control clamp

wash

thermometer 195 degrees F.

to drain

warm

cool

cold

500 watt sol- dering iron unit with tip removed

vent for resi- due drain

water flow is adjusted so con- denser is cold at bot- tom, cool in middle and warm at top

residue

distillate

Figure 11:

CONTINUOUS RUN STILL

also called "sneaky home still"

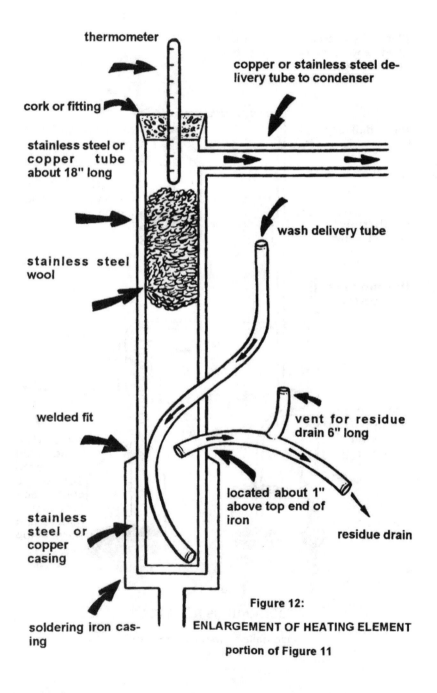

thermometer

copper or stainless steel delivery tube to condenser

cork or fitting

stainless steel or copper tube about 18" long

stainless steel wool

wash delivery tube

welded fit

vent for residue drain 6" long

located about 1" above top end of iron

stainless steel or copper casing

residue drain

soldering iron casing

Figure 12:

ENLARGEMENT OF HEATING ELEMENT

portion of Figure 11

5-42 Notice that the soldering iron tip has been removed and replaced by the stainless steel reflux column. The whole system operates in a precarious balance between two controls; the wash flow control clamp on a rubber section of the wash delivery tube, and the faucet, which controls the condenser cooling rate.

5-43 The wash flow clamp adjustment is the most precarious one. The siphon is started by blowing in the siphon vent tube until a few drops of the liquid come out the Residue Drain Tube. Then it is pinched off until the temperature reaches 195F/91C or thereabouts on the thermometer. At this point the flow rate is adjusted by trial and error until the temperature settles in at around 195F/91C. It will then continue to run and distill until all of the wash is gone.

5-44 The wash jar can be filled many times over while the still is in operation to give a continuous running still, if desired. Eventually, it will have to be shut down for cleaning. A little lower temperature than 195F say 190F/88C, will yield a faster run, but the concentration of Ethanol will be less. A single run through this still will produce alcohol of at least 100 proof (50 percent). This type of still is not well suited for multiple runs as it is a delicately balanced operation. But it is very well suited for single runs. Any other adjustable heat source could be substituted for the soldering iron. Diagrams of this still are found in figures 11 and 12.

He only drinks to calm his nerves,

and his steadiness to improve.

One day he got so steady

He couldn't even move.

Chapter 6: Fermented Beverages

BEER & WINE FUNDAMENTALS

6-1 Now that we have covered everything the book title obligates us to cover, we can sit back, relax, and talk about alcoholic beverages that you **CAN LEGALLY** make in tour own home--without hassle and *Tax Free.*

FOR PERSONAL USE & CONSUMPTION

6-2 In the United States any single adult (adult by state legal standards) can make wine or beer for personal use and consumption. This is a Federal law and applies so long as no state law prohibits it. Almost all states allow the free production of home wine and beer. However, check with you own state authorities or you local home wine supplies store as laws have a way of changing from time to time. A husband and wife can make up to 200 gallons of wine or beer per year. So there is no reason to run dry. 200 gallons per year means more than 2 quarts per day! In Canada and Great Britain there are similar laws whose end goal is to avoid taxing citizens as commercial businesses.

6-3 And in **ALL** countries there are the professional "righteousness" groups which need to be fought to a draw if possible. These groups lobby their representatives and everybody else's representative to legislate every private act into a public crime if it does not square with their own rigid agenda. Having summarized these few legal matters it is time to leave all that behind us.

FERMENTATION

6-4 Both wine and beer begin as fermentation. To set the record straight, lets define a few terms. FERMENTATION is the primary means by which most drinkable alcohol is produced. Fermentation is easily started by using almost any fruit, flower or vegetable juice and a yeast. What is fermentation? And, for that matter, what is yeast?

6-5 YEASTS are microscopic plants that are all around us in the air, much like pollen except smaller. Yeasts are NOT bacteria. Bacteria are small microscopic animals. So yeasts and bacteria exist on a small (microscopic) scale much as animals and plants exist on a large (macroscopic)   scale.

6-6 Which brings us back to fermentation. Yeasts feed primarily on diets rich in some carbohydrates (sugars) and, like all plants, need phosphates and nitrogen to prosper. When yeasts are flourishing in a heavily sugared environment (such as fruit juices) they keep their life processes going by assimilating the sugar and breaking it down into Equal amounts of Carbon Dioxide (which bubbles off as a gas) and Ethyl Alcohol (which is the drinkable kind and stays in solution). This process of yeast growth is called Fermentation. Fermentation is the process by which all wine and beer and most alcoholic beverages of ANY kind, are produced; whiskey, gin, vodka, scotch, etc. start out this way.

6-7 If you start your fermentation using a grain such as barley and then bottle the fermented product before it is completely through fermenting, it builds up pressure inside the bottle (from the fermentation which releases the inert gas Carbon Dioxide). The result is usually called Beer although the same process is used for making champagne or sparkling wine. Beer is lower than wine in alcoholic content because the amount of Barley used in the drink is kept low intentionally. Most beer also uses a malting process, as described previously, and many have HOPS added.

6-8 On the other hand if you start your fermentation with a liquid richer in sugars using any vegetable, fruit, or grain as a base and simply let it ferment out completely, or nearly so, a higher alcoholic yield will result and it may be called a Wine. The usual fermented beer contains about 3 percent to 8 percent alcohol. Wine is normally anywhere from 8 percent to 20 percent alcohol.

MAKING WINE

6-9 To learn to make a good wine you can start with a kit for the first few batches until experience is gained. These kits contain their own instructions. In this section we will give a brief outline of the steps necessary to prepare your own wine starting from a frozen fruit juice concentrate. Orange juice makes a good choice as it is reasonable well balanced for wine making and produces an excellent light wine very similar to white grape. We will outline the instruction for a single gallon. If you wish to make 4 or 5 gallons, or a number of liters, merely multiply the recipe in the usual manner.

6-10 Start with enough cans of concentrate to make 5 quarts or liters. A liter, by the way, is about 10% larger than a quart. This is plenty close enough for our usage and, in small lot production, the two can even be considered the same. Use the directions on the concentrate can for the proper ratio of concentrate to water. Do not mix with water yet. Open the cans of concentrate and place the contents in a large open container (polyethylene plastic or stainless steel). Add 4 full cups of cane sugar. A US cup is 8 oz liquid so this would be about a quarter liter. Four FULL cups would add up to a very heaping liter.

6-11 To this add 3 quarts of very hot water and stir the mixture to dissolve the sugar and thaw the concentrates. After this is thoroughly mixed and dissolved, add enough water to bring the total in your pan or container to 5 quarts or liters. This is your basic Must as it is now called. You can throw in the  peeling from a freshly peeled orange or apple if you have one available. Don't throw in the whole wastebasket.

6-12 You will need to purchase some Campden tablets (or sulphite) and some wine yeasts from a Home Wine Supply store. Add one campden tablet (after first crushing it to a powder) and stir it into the must. Stir the must well, cover it loosely and leave sit for about 24 hours. Then add your wine yeast. Shake or mix thoroughly again. Cover loosely with a clean cloth, lid or aluminum foil.

6-13 Fermentation will commence within a day or two. Keep temperature about 70-75 degrees F. It is not absolutely necessary to stir or mix again, but you can stir gently every day or two for the first few days. After about 10 days to 2 weeks the fermentation should have settled down to where it is unnoticeable. At this time carefully pour or siphon the liquid through a funnel fitted with a coarse nylon bottom of the container. The remaining liquid can then be put into fa narrow mouth jug or jar of the proper size which, in turn, can be fitted with a fermentation lock or simply capped loosely (Do no ever tightly cap or close a fermenting container). Fermentation locks work well and can be purchased from your local Home Wine Supply store.

6-14 If you are going to use the same open container again (instead of a narrow-neck jar and fermentation lock), cover the surface of the liquid with a sheet of plastic-film or wax paper before replacing the lid or cover (remember - *cover loosely!*) This plastic film or wax paper should be replaced about once a week, and will serve to keep the surface air from contacting your wine.

6-15 Siphon the wine off the dregs again about three weeks later and then again in another three weeks. If kept in a cool place (But Not Cold!) during this time, the wine should clear by itself (about 65-70F/18-21C.) As soon as the wine has sufficiently cleared, it can be bottled. It should taste tart or acidic---similar to in-sufficiently sweetened lemonade. Your wine can be drunk anytime after the third or fourth week---even before it has cleared---but the longer you wait the better it will be.

PRESERVING YOUR WINE'S FLAVOR

6-16 Most modern recipes call for a short initial vigorous fermentation with only a loose covering over your wine (lid or cloth), followed by a longer period of slow fermentation when the wine is protected to a greater degree (by an air lock) from coming into contact with the free air. This first period usually lasts from 1 to 2 weeks and is termed the Primary Fermentation. The second period covers anywhere from a few weeks to a few months depending on the recipe, temperature, etc. and is called the Secondary Fermentation.

6-17 The Primary Fermentation is marked by a bubbly appearance and usually vigorous frothing at the top. The Secondary Fermentation is the longer period of slow activity. During the primary fermentation most recipes do not encourage you to protect the surface of the liquid from the air. There is good reason for this. If the fermentation is quite brisk it may bubble up over the top of the container and through a fermentation lock, if one is used. This creates quite a mess and for no good reason. Since carbon dioxide is a fair amount heavier than air, the carbon dioxide that is trapped in the bubbly frothing surface of the Primary Fermentation provides its own protection from the air.

6-18 Following this period of high activity, however, not much carbon dioxide is produced and very little froth. Thus the slightest air currents in a room will penetrate through the thin carbon dioxide layer on the surface of the wine and allow the wine to come into direct contact with the oxygen in the air. This is usually not desired. Thus during Secondary Fermentation it is wise to either use an air lock (fermentation lock) such as the common plastic type sold in most wine supply stores or some other method of protecting the surface.

6-19 A large open container such as a crock or plastic container can be used for the Primary Fermentation and a narrow mouthed container, such as a jug, can be used for the Secondary Fermentation. It is customary during the Primary Fermentation period of a week or so to keep the open container covered with a fitting lid or plastic sheet. This protects the must from dust, dirt, flying insects etc. At the end of the Primary Fermentation, the must can be transferred to a narrow mouth container. The new container is filled to within an inch or so of the top leaving only a very small surface area in contact with the inside atmosphere of the bottle. The top of the narrow mouth is then fitted with a fermentation lock mounted in a cork or cap or with a loose fitting, but complete, closure.

6-20 The shape or style of the containers used is not important. For instance, if you have only a narrow mouth plastic or glass container available you can use if for the primary and secondary fermentation by cleaning it each time before you rack the Must and replace the liquid for further fermentation. A fermentation lock, or other closure, does not need to be fitted on it for the first week or so.

6-21 Similarly an open container can be used throughout the fermentation. However, since it is difficult to fit on a tight sealing fermentation lock on large mouth containers, some protection can be

loose plastic cover   **cotton plug**   **thumper**   **glass or plastic air lock.**

(preferred method)

afforded by cutting a piece of wax paper or plastic wrap to the inside shape of the container and simply floating this on the surface of the liquid to exclude contact with the air. The tiny amount of liquid exposed between the edge of the paper or plastic and the container's inside edges will not matter if the top of the container is covered with a loose fitting lid or cloth or plastic sheet to exclude air currents.

6-22 Each time the Must is racked new wax paper or plastic should be put down. Another solution is to cut a thin wooden lid the size of the inside of the container and Float this on the surface of the liquid. This makes a splendid solution since if it is made from oak it will have some of the effects of aging in oak. It should be boiled thoroughly before using. Plywood should never be used as it has glues and resins which will contaminate your wine. If you use a large plastic open container that has an air-tight snap-on lid be sure to simply place the lid on Loosely after you have floated your wax paper or oak board. Never, Never tightly cap a fermenting vessel unless you like to clean up burst containers.

MAKING BEER

6-23 For making a single gallon of lager beer, use a malt extract, lightly hopped, or a similar malt extract. Malt Extract can be purchased at your local home wine store and is also available in some grocery stores. A good beer yeast should be purchased. Mix together about 5 ounces (150 grams) of malt extract (about 1/2 cup) with 1 quart/liter boiling water and 2 1/2 level cups of sugar. Boil together for a few minutes, Stirring Constantly until all has been dissolved. next, pour this mixture (called Wort) into your large open container for fermenting. Add 4 quarts or liters of Cold Water. Mix thoroughly and allow to cool to room temperature, or about 70-80F/21-27C (feels tepid to touch). if your added water was cool then it should be at room temperature almost immediately. Add the contents of the yeast packet, mix well, and immediately transfer the Wort to a cool place (about 60F/16C.)

6-24 *Now comes the most important part for making good lager beer*--a cool place for the fermentation to take place (not below 40F/5C degrees, or above 70F/21C degrees). Fermenting at lower temperatures will take somewhat longer than a higher temperatures. The ideal temperature is 60F/16C degrees during the first week of fermentation.

6-25 After about 12 to 24 hours, the beer should have active frothing surface. This bubbling may last from 5 to 10 days depending on the temperature. When the bubbling has stopped, remove the froth from the top carefully (do not agitate the container too much as the Dregs, or sediment, on the bottom will be stirred up and make your beer cloudy). After clearing the top of the liquid, siphon the clear liquid into another container, being careful to leave the dregs behind.

6-26 Put the new container in a vary cool place again (this time the temperature can even be below 40F/5C degrees, but keep it above freezing). Put a piece of wax paper or plastic sheet on the surface of the liquid to keep off the oxygen. Within three or four days the liquid should be fairly clear. Siphon carefully once again.

PRIMING AND BOTTLING

6-27 To **Prime** (Priming is the act of adding sugar directly before bottling so that the additional small amount of fermentation produced will add the carbonation needed for "sparkle") your beer, remove about a pint (half liter) of the new beer and dissolve in it 2 level tablespoons of sugar. Pour the pint back in the main batch, and stir it gently. Be sure it is mixed well, or you will run the risk of bursting bottles. Bottle Immediately After Adding Sugar.

6-28 Use standard beer bottles or any other bottle which you can securely cap or close. Crown caps usually present the best solution to this problem. Fill the bottles to within about an inch of the top. Cap and store Upright in a Warm place (70-80F/21-27C). It is best to store your bottles for the first few weeks in a place where a burst bottle won't hurt anyone or anything. This is a rare occurrence, but one worth guarding against. The beer can be drunk in a few weeks, but a month or two gives a better tasting beer.

Bottle Caps before and after being crimped on bottle.

6-29 Chill beer before serving. *KEEP IN AN UPRIGHT POSITION* in refrigerator. Handle gently to avoid stirring up any sediment. Pour slowly and smoothly into a glass large enough to hold the contents of the bottle. When the powder on the bottom of the bottle starts to pour out, stop pouring, and discard the remainder.

6-30 The longer a beer is stored before drinking, the better the sediment stays on the bottom of the bottle. It eventually may form a thin firm crust that will not rise when the beer is poured out. Sediment, by the way, is not harmful to drink; on the contrary it is extremely rich in B vitamins and iron. Thus the avoidance of consuming sediment or allowing it to stir up into the drink is largely a cosmetic affair.

6-31 This chapter only briefly describes the many processes involved in Wine and Beer making. For a thorough treatment of this subject, the reader is advised to read the book **BEER & WINE PRODUCTION** For Farm and Home published by Noguska,LLC 741 N. Countyline St., Fostoria, Ohio 44830.

DON'T EVEN THINK ABOUT

DRINKING PURE ETHANOL

IT IS A VIOLENT POISON!!

Chapter 7: Other Beverages

All it really does is make drip coffee ..... but it looks so impressive people gladly pay $12.00 a cup!!

7-1 This could easily be the largest chapter in the book - but it's not going to be. There are so many beverages - both alcoholic and otherwise - that we are going to need to sort through these and mention only those with some degree of popularity or uniqueness. To make it convenient for the reader we are going to compact this · information by alphabetizing the beverage names followed by a brief description.

7-2 A breakdown of the different types of, say, wines, beers, gins, mixed drinks, etc. is included in the Alcoholic Beverage Guide in Chapter 9.

7-3 The drinks we shall discuss in this chapter each falls into a generalized category of its own. Some are alcoholic and some not, but somewhere in the world each one is considered a palatable and desirable drink.

7-4 All potable beverages consist of water plus additives. The additives determine the character of the drink. Not only the type of additive but how it is treated either before, during or after it is added. For instance if you boil green coffee beans in water the drink will have little if any resemblance to a drink that uses the same beans toasted and coarsely ground.

7-5 APERITIF - Do not confuse with aperitive which is a mild laxative. An aperitif is much like a liqueur, but it is not generally based on a distilled product as is a liqueur. Flavorings, etc. are added to a basic

wine or fortified wine. Fortified means that the wine has had some extra pure alcohol added to it so that the alcoholic content is enhanced over the natural item. Vermouth is the best example of an Aperitif and it is sometimes fortified.

7-6 BEER - A fermented beverage that derives from the fermentation of a malted grain, such as corn, barley, rice, etc. Usually the base used is wholly or mostly barley. The alcoholic content is given in both percent

by volume and percent by weight - but usually the latter. There is a difference. The alcoholic content of beer by volume is in the range of 3 percent to 8 percent, with most about 4 or 5 percent. See table D in Chapter 9 for comparison with percentage by weight.

7-7 CIDER - Unfermented apple juice.

7-8 COFFEE - Coffee originated in the Arabian countries and then spread rapidly throughout the world. Most of the U.S. coffee is a direct descendent of a single coffee plant that was brought to the New World in 1723. It is a refreshing beverage which, like tea, owes its stimulating qualities to the presence of caffeine.

7-9 CORDIAL - Sometimes used to mean a liqueur, this usage is incorrect. A cordial is merely an extracted fruit juice made into a syrup by adding sweets or rendering down. If it is not too thick or syrupy, it can be used as a sweet drink by itself. Cordials are used as basic flavor additives for other drinks. They can be made naturally from fruit products or artificially and are non-alcoholic by themselves.

7-10 KEPHIR - Also Kefir. The same as Koumis, but usually started with cow's milk instead of camel or mare milk.

7-11 KOUMIS - A mildly alcoholic beverage popular with northern Asiatic tribes. Contains about 2 percent alcohol and when distilled is called Arika. Normally lactose (milk sugar) is not fermentable. However, Koumis is made from Mare or Camel milk by the action of Lactase (an enzyme) which breaks lactose down to its simpler constituents glucose and galactose, both of which are fermentable.

7-12 LIQUEUR - Note the spelling. Sometimes applied to a very few wines and distilled liquor of very high quality. This is not its common meaning, however. The typical liqueur starts with a basic distilled liquor. To this is added intense or unusual flavoring and perfumes. France was an innovator in this area and many of the most popular extracts used today are French. Some popular extracts are mint, angelica, sassafras, lemon, orange, peppermint, cinnamon, tea, coffee, etc. Many times artificial flavors, colors and edible perfumes are used.

7-13 LIQUOR - An alcoholic beverage from about 50 to 190 proof, but usually no higher than 120 proof. Distilled from a mash or a wine, its main flavor is derived from the constituents of the basic mash from which it is distilled plus the slight "contaminants" introduced during aging from contact with a wooden barrel or other container, plus the actual chemical changes occurring during aging. Few or no direct additives are used in the distilled product. Whiskey, Vodka, and Gin are good examples.

7-14 PERRY - Unfermented pear juice. Same as CIDER for apples.

7-15 POP WINE - Normal wine has its flavoring ingredients added before fermentation begins. If a neutral base, such as sugar and nutrients, is fermented out and THEN the flavoring added, the result is a Pop Wine. It is not appreciably different from an ordinary mixed drink such as a Tom Collins, Screwdriver, etc., depending on the fruit juice or flavor added.

7-16 SPIRIT - Sometimes used to denote either pure alcohol or the alcoholic portion of a liquor. More generally, Spirit is used in the same sense as liquor, and the two are used interchangeably.

7-17 SYRUP - See Cordial.

7-18 TEA - Tea throughout the world comes from the same basic plant. Differences in tea names, such as orange, orange pekoe, black, green, etc., come about from using different processing. Black tea is processed by fermentation. Green tea is unfermented. The bulk of the world's tea is grown in the Asiatic countries such as Ceylon and India. It owes its popularity to the presence of a chemical class of compounds, caffeine, which are stimulants.

7-19 WINE - A fermented beverage using any grain, fruit or cereal as its base. If it is not made from grapes the word Wine should be qualified with an adjective such as Apple Wine, Blackberry Wine, etc. If no adjective appears, it is commonly understood to be Grape Wine.

The alcoholic content is given in percent terms and is usually in the range of 10 to 21 percent by volume. Anything over 12 or 13% is probably FORTIFIED wine; that is, extra pure alcohol has been added to increase the alcohol percentage above that possible or practical by fermentation alone.

Chapter 8: Lores & Legends

"Why hello there!......Do you jog for your health too??"

8-1 Almost every activity of leisure human endeavor, save perhaps eating and sleeping, is in some manner regulated, legislated, or moralized against. Sex, alcoholic beverages, dancing, card-playing, gambling, theatre attending and even just plain conversation or quiet reading have all had their doomsayers and attackers. Our concern in this book is only with Ethanol and its production. There are quite enough tales of the chased and the chastened in this narrow area to fill a few volumes - and indeed more than several have been written.

MOONSHINERS

8-2 It is hard to determine exactly where the word moonshine originated. Every source has its own theory, but the name is descriptive enough of the secretive nature of the operation. According to George Simpson in **A BOOK ABOUT A THOUSAND THINGS** (Harper, 1946) it did **NOT** originate in the hills of Kentucky or Tennessee, or even in America at all, as is commonly thought. Simpson cites a dictionary published in London in 1785 which defines moonshine as illicit BRANDY which was smuggled at night into Great Britain from France and the Netherlands. There goes another tale of old that's not as told!

8-3 In the United States the Bureau of ALCOHOL, TOBACCO & FIREARMS (BATF) is charged with enforcing the liquor laws, as an arm of the Treasury Department. Their prime interest is in enforcing the law as it affects the collection of taxes by the Treasury Department. According to Mr. Rex Davis, a retired BATF chief, "moon shining" is not nearly so widespread as it once was and for most practical purposes can be said to be well under control. It is essentially one of those problems that helps to solve itself. The basic ingredients are not as cheap as they once were, people are more affluent nowadays and the taxes on alcohol have not risen in step with inflation. Thus the enormous profit margins are no longer there.

8-4 Mr. Davis also laid some other myths to rest by stating that the historical areas of moon shining such as Kentucky, Tennessee and W. Virginia are no longer producers of any great amounts. If there is any concentration worthy of the name it is in the middle and lower Atlantic seaboard around the Carolinas.

8-5 But in days not long gone the activity was aplenty. Especially during downturns in the economy, such as the Great Depression. It is also true that when an area votes itself "dry" (such as many do under the local option plans) the moon shining activities increase greatly in that immediate area.

8-6 Some of the early and surprising aspects of moon shining were the ground rules that slowly grew up. During the late 1800's and early 1900's it was not unusual for an arrest at a still site to be a deadly confrontation between two armed groups: the federals and the moonshiners. As could be expected, the Federal Government with infinitely greater resources at its command, is not going to take the shooting of its agent lightly. Harsh prison sentences are handed down when gunfire is brought into play.

8-7 During one of these periods of conflict, in the early part of this century, a group of clergymen who were friendly with both sides in the combat got together and helped bring about a decline in the warfare. The moonshiners didn't stop distilling and the feds didn't stop looking for them. The clergymen made the point to the moonshiners that the Feds weren't going to prosecute anybody if they couldn't find anybody at the still. Since they were going to lose their still if the Agents found them,

Large still impounded during a "moonshine" raid in Oklahoma

no matter what, both sides would be better off alive than dead. After this period a new tactic on the part of the moonshiners gradually evolved. When they were discovered they ran like a streak of lightning. Presuming they could outrun the Agents, that was the end of it usually.

8-8 But of course every new weapon is met with a counter-weapon. The tale is told of a moonshiner named Charlie Potts that was found dead-to-rights with his still cooker burning brightly. Charlie took one look at the agents and took off through the woods. One of the Agents in the raiders, nick-named Big-six, had been an outstanding college athlete and couldn't resist the challenge and the chase. Big-six took off after Charlie and chased him up and down through the fields, over the fences and down every byway known to Charlie Potts. Big-six finally caught up with Charlie and collared him, but they both collapsed from exhaustion after the capture. And no wonder. His fellow agents found that Big-six and Charlie had run full speed at least two miles over rocky, rough and hilly terrain!

8-9 More recently a case in California reads almost like a Keystone Kops comedy. A Federal Agent gained the confidence of several bootleggers and posed as a big buyer for the underground. The moonshiners sold him a small amount of alcohol and he went on his way. However, after a discrete wait of a few days, other agents moved in and arrested the bootleggers.

8-10 The trapped bootleggers still were not aware that the original "underworld character" that bought from them was a Federal Agent. So while they were awaiting sentencing to prison the first agent
contacted them, still posing as an underworld buyer, and asked to do business with them when their prison sentences were up. They both readily agreed. After they were released the Agent set up productions schedules with them and even helped them get their still going; going so far as buying them a ton of sugar with government vouchers.

8-11 When all was finally going good and the still was producing successfully, the Agent stepped in and SURPRISE arrested them all. Imagine their shock. However this second arrest did not hold up in court. It was thrown out because the agent had used ENTRAPMENT. Essentially the statutes on entrapment say that you can arrest a man for breaking the law but you can't encourage or help him to break the law and then arrest him! Recently some courts have looked the other way when entrapment is somehow related to drug traffic. We seem to be drifting back to an "ends justify the means" philosophy once again.

8-12 Almost every conceivable reason is used by moonshiners to excuse their conduct. In a recent case in Ohio a moonshiner claimed that his wife was an alcoholic and he couldn't afford to keep her in spirits. He went to jail and she, presumably, started paying more for her habit. Others have claimed that they were only walking by and saw the still just before the agents arrived! It was a common practice of some of the more unscrupulous operators to find a young relative to act as a helper. Then when a bust occurred the youngster would claim the still was his and get off on probation or, at worst, with a very light sentence.

8-13 Once arrested for distilling alcohol your troubles are hardly over with your prison sentence. For almost any other crime imaginable including murder, rape, assault, riot or mayhem, the case would stop with your sentencing. But if you are caught distilling in your garage or basement you go to prison AND you lose your home, your car and all of your possessions that are anywhere located on these premises. They will all be sold at public auction. Recently this has been expanded to drug cases of any kind. It is not unlikely that within another few decades anyone convicted of any crime will forfeit everything of value they own. If so for alcohol why not for drugs?; if so for drugs why not for murder?; if so for murder why not for burglary?; if so for burglary why not for shoplifting? The drift in "logic" is slow but unmistakable.

8-14 It is one of those incredible and bizarre overkill laws that occur whenever the enormous power to totally annihilate or confiscate is concentrated in a governing body and used irresponsibly. It is unworthy of the dignity of the government of which we all are so justifiably proud.

8-15 Along this same line the agents of the BATF are blamed for some of the more unsavory statutes which they are responsible for enforcing. It is the legislature that makes the laws and batteries of high-priced consultant lawyers and political appointees that write the statutes. If the tax laws were not enforced the inequality that now exists in how the tax load is shared might be even worse.

> *If ten percent alky is good*
>
> *then nitro packed under the hood*
>
> *must certainly be great*
>
> *though I discovered too late*
>
> *tthe difference between can-do and should.*

8-16 It is unfortunate that the legislature has decided to invade the private household and forbid you to distill for your own private usage. As we have commented before, this is NOT true of tobacco and other items which are also taxed. But changing this condition will be up to the legislature and that is where the battle will need to be fought.

8-17 Before this chapter ends it should not go unmentioned those in recent years the individual has been getting back some fair portions of these rights which were snatched away many years ago. The much-maligned legislature has been responsible and to them we should be grateful. Remember, for the most part, it was NOT your PRESENT legislator who took these rights away in the first place. Maybe there is such a thing as progress, haphazard though it might be!

PART II

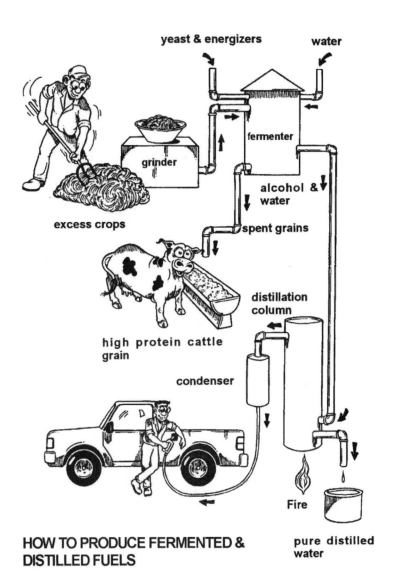

yeast & energizers   water

fermenter

grinder

alcohol & water

excess crops

spent grains

high protein cattle grain

distillation column

condenser

Fire

HOW TO PRODUCE FERMENTED & DISTILLED FUELS

pure distilled water

Chapter 9:
Gasohol & Ethanol

NO! WAIT! STOP! We don't want to BUST it. We want to BUY it!

GASOHOL

9-1 It surprises most of us to learn that GASOHOL is nothing new. It was first conceived over 50 years ago. During the depression days many books, pamphlets and University Research papers were written on the subject. It was well explored and widely publicized (for the times). Then why are we only now in a panic to develop it? Ah, thereby hangs a tale by the tail!

9-2 One of the aspects of free democracies (as presently developed) is they operate primarily from crisis to crisis. In this we can't blame the other fellow; we can't blame the oil interests; we can't blame the government; and we can't blame the auto companies. It is we, ourselves! You and I and countless others (well, actually a little over 250 million) just like us. We will not spend 6 hours, say, growing grain and fermenting it when we can spend two hours drilling a hole in the ground for the same end result: fuel. No argument about future generations will ever sway present generations when it actually comes down to doing the work.

9-3 We are actually at the point where it takes about 6 hours work either way--grow the fuel or drill for fuel. Although it is even-steven right now, not many years ago it was MUCH cheaper to drill the hole. Perhaps grain alcohol isn't the final answer. But it is a workable answer for right now. Until we can either perfect its production or come up with some superior alternatives, it can do the job.

9-4 We have no solutions for the much bigger problem of why we, as a nation, continually paint ourselves into economic corners. Perhaps it is the fault of the institutions we build to serve us. Ask your friendly corner Political Scientist or Economic Adviser. He can be working on that problem while we are trying to solve this one. We have already taken far more time than we can afford to castigate the shortfalls in our social structures.

9-5 Prior to World War II, many European countries were requiring the use of GASOHOL to conserve dwindling supplies of petroleum. In 1931 the Philippines sold a blend of gasoline, alcohol and ethyl ether. They called it **GASONOL** and special motors were designed to burn it efficiently. In the early 1930's Germany mandated a 10 percent alcohol, 90 percent gasoline blend - exactly the same blend advocated so widely even yet. The first large undertaking in the United States was also to produce a 10-90 mix. This was in Atchison, Kansas during 1934. The operation failed before the start of World War II. It nearly succeeded, however, in spite of a number of disadvantages. They called the mixture **AGROL** for **AGR**icultural alcohOL. It represented one of the many early attempts by farmers to exert some control over the product of their labors.

9-6 It is difficult to determine just who coined the term **GASOHOL** for the first time. **GASOHOL** is defined as a mixture of gasoline and alcohol. The alcohol can be Ethanol (Grain Alcohol) or Methanol (Wood Alcohol), or even higher alcohols (see Table II). Ethanol is readily produced from easily fermentable materials and, at present, this is the alcohol usually blended to produce **GASOHOL.** We have discussed the production of Ethanol in Chapter 4 (fermentation) and the concentration of Ethanol in Chapter 5 (distillation). We will now explore the additional things we need to be aware of for Ethanol production as a gasoline additive and as a complete fuel itself. **9-1**

I am always at a loss to know how much to believe of my own stories.

Washington Irving 1783-1859

TABLE I

Properties of Aliphatic Hydrocarbons
Found in Petroleum and Natural Gas
This chart is for the normal isomer
This table is similar to the one in Chapter 3 but includes more useful data

Formula	Chemical Name	Physical State	Boiling Point F/C	Common Name	% From Crude Oil Fractionation
CH4	Methane	Gas	-258/-161	Natural Gas	23%
C2H6	Ethane		-126.4/-88		
C3H8	Propane		-51/-46		
C4H10	Butane		30.2/1		
C5H12	Pentane	Liquid	96.8/36	High Grade Naptha	
C6H14	Hexane		156/69		
C7H16	Heptane		208/98	Gasoline	
C8H18	Octane		259/126		
C9H20	Nonane		302/150		
C10H22	Decane		345/174		
C11H24	Undecane		383/195		14%
C12H26	Dodecane		419/215	Kerosene	
C13H30	Tridecane		453/234	Fuel Oil	44%
C14H30	Tetradecane		487/253	Lubricating Oil mixtures of higher	13%
C15H32	Pentadecane		520/271		
C20H42	Elcosane	Solid	amorphous	Paraffin	3%
C60H122	Hexacontane				

NOTE: Remaining 3% is lost

NOTE: These approximate fractions are from a simple fractionating column. By the use of catalysts and specialized processes, more than 50% of the crude can be converted to gasoline if this is desired. Or, conversely, less can be converted.

9-7 GASOHOL is by nature a stopgap. It is not an ultimate solution to any problem. ALCOHOL, by itself, may be an ultimate solution, but at this writing that has yet to be proven. GASOHOL is not an ultimate solution because it is a mixture of a non-replenishable resource (gasoline) with a replenishable resource (alcohol). Even worse, the mixture usually has much much more of the non-replenishable resource (90 percent). When petroleum supplies become very scarce or dry up entirely, which they are bound to do, GASOHOL will be over and done with. But for the present it does extend our supplies of gasoline by 10 percent which is important.

9-8 Gasoline is not a single compound, such as Ethanol or Methanol, but is a mixture of many compounds. Alcohol and gasoline have different vapor pressures (ability to evaporate). Many of the constituents of gasoline actually boil at temperatures not much above room level. This is especially true of gasoline blended for winter time usage. Refineries adjust their mix or blend to correspond to the seasons. In winter the blend has more of the lighter hydrocarbons in the naptha range.

9-9 See Table I for a comparison of the hydrocarbon products resulting from the distilling or cracking of petroleum. Table I lists the typical products that result from the simple fractional distillation of petroleum oil in a refinery. Refer to Chapter 5 for a description of this process. The compounds at the top of the table are the first to evaporate. The further down the list you go the further up the fractionating column the product comes off. During the summer the blend is again changed. THe napthas are dropped and more of the higher boiling products are included. In the fall and spring a compromise blend is produced.

9-10 TABLE II lists the simple alcohols in the same ascending order of complexity and density as Table I does for simple petroleum products. These tables are the same as tables I and II in Chapter 3, but contain more detail. A reference to these tables now and then while reading this chapter may help your understanding - if not your enjoyment.

Some men are like musical glasses: to produce their finest notes you must keep them wet.
Samuel Taylor Coleridge 1772-1834

TABLE II
Properties of Simple Alcohols
This chart is for the normal isomer

ALCOHOL	FORMULA	PHYSICAL STATE	BOILING POINT F/C	FREEZING POINT F/C	SOLU-BILITY IN WATER
Methyl Methanol	CH3OH	Liquid	149/65	-144/98	Yes
Ethyl Ethanol	C2H5OH		172.4/78	-179/-117	Yes
Propyl Etc.	C3H7OH		208/98	-197/-127	Yes
Butyl	C4H9OH		244/118	-128/-89	about 10
Pentyl	C5H11OH		280/138	-108/-78	a few
Hexyl	C6H13OH		313/156	-62/-52	slight
Dodecyl	C12H25OH		491/254	73/23	insoluble

This table is similar to the one in Chapter 3 but includes more useful data.
*Physical State at 68F / 20C

9-11 What are some of the advantages and disadvantages of a 10 percent mixture of GASOHOL?   A 10 percent mixture has one overriding advantage. You don't notice the difference between burning a 10 percent mixture and burning pure gasoline. No adjustments to your carburetor or motor need be made. The driving characteristics such as pick-up, stall, etc. will not be altered enough to be noticeable. This is a big advantage during a transition period when millions, perhaps billions, of motors (car, boat, tractor, cycle, mower, power plant, truck, train, etc., etc.) are already produced and designed for gasoline or diesel use. The cost of converting these simultaneously to a different fuel would be prohibitive - even if it could be done .... which it can't!

GASOHOL & WATER

9-12 It is reliably reported that the 10 percent ethanol in GASOHOL actually improves the burning of the gasoline. A cleaner exhaust may result. Water in a gasohol mixture can be very disturbing, however.

When pure ethanol and gasoline are mixed, the ethanol has practically no contact with the air (it is only 10 percent of the solution and is surrounded by gasoline molecules). Therefore it does not tend to draw water from the air. But if water gets into the tank by condensation or otherwise, the water acts as an entraining agent for the Ethanol (makes it separate from the gasoline).

9-13 A surprisingly small amount of water - even as little as 1 or 2 percent can entrain (or capture) all of the ethanol. The problem here is not that the ethanol won't burn with this slight amount of water in it. Rather, the problem is the ethanol is no longer evenly dispersed throughout the gasoline. It is concentrated in a pocket and when this pocket of nearly pure ethanol hits your fuel intake line it goes through a carburetor that is adjusted for gasoline (gasohol) and not adjusted for pure ethanol. The mixture is too lean as alcohol needs an air to fuel ratio of 9:1 (10 percent alcohol) and not 14.5:1 (6 percent gasoline) as does gasoline. Therefore the motor misses, sputters and coughs.

9-14 Ten percent **GASOHOL** buys time. Time for planning. Time for experimentation. Time for learning. Time for the more painful psychological readjustments for you and me. Life will not be harsher or less fun after we develop new and different fuels and adjust to them. It will be different. But to imagine that we are going backward in time is folly. We are simply taking steps now that could and should have been taken by our ancestors a few short generations back. But before we pat ourselves on the back for our own great foresight, consider two things:

1. *We were forced into it ourselves, as a society, even though we were fully aware it was coming and even knew when.*

2. *Future generations are going to lament this generations inability to come to grips with a whole panoply of similar problems that are even now staring us all in the face .... and each problem will come to a crisis stage in its own time - just like this one - before anything is done about it.*

---

*Compute these percentages by dividing the amount of air by the total amount of gas. This is 1/(9+1) = 1/10 and NOT 1/9. Actually, the 14.5:1 figure is for pure gasoline. As it turns out, the addition of ethanol to the gasoline in producing gasohol make the fuel-air mixture more tolerant. That is, it is not as critical as it was for pure gasoline. Another added advantage of gasohol. The engine is easier to tune and keep in tune.

The president of the company needed a new secretary so he hired a psychologist to help him make the proper selection.

Three women were interviewed and the psychologist asked them all the same question: "Two and two make what together?.

The first woman answered "Four"

The second woman answered "It could be 22"

The third woman answered "It could be 4 or it could be 22"

After the women left the psychologist turned to the President and exclaimed "The first woman gave the expected answer, the second sensed a trap and the third was going to go for the best of bother worlds.

Which one will it be?

The president waited a moment and then said thoughtfully "The brown eyed brunette!"

9-15 Discouraging? Not at all. Human nature. And "Human Nature" can and does change. But the change is so slow, and our 70 to 100 year life span is so short in the scheme of things, that we can't even discern it. Write a note to your great-great-great-great-grandkids. Ask them how much change - really basic change - they see since your day. By then it should be discernible. Just barely, but still discernible.

ABSOLUTE ALCOHOL

9-16 Now let us go to the other extreme and consider pure or nearly pure alcohol. Prior to this time we have used the proof concept for Ethanol as a carryover from the beverage alcohol discussion. From this point forward we will consider percentages. The proof concept is an artificial concept and has no real value. It certainly has no place in a technical discussion.

9-17 Pure Ethanol is difficult to produce from the fermentation-distillation process. This was discussed in chapter 3. To obtain purity much beyond about 95 percent, such things as benzene or lime (CaO) must be added and then the product redistilled. 100 percent Ethanol is called Absolute Alcohol.

I9-18 t is to noted that fermentation is not the only way to produce Ethanol. Early in this century chemists perfected a way to produce High quality Ethanol from Ethylene. Ethylene is one of the common byproducts of fractional distillation of petroleum when making gasoline. Although this method has been used to produce as much as 60 percent of this nation's Ethanol in the past, it is, to us today, a dead-end process. This is because the source of Ethylene is the very same source we are striving so hard to be independent of: petroleum.

9-19 Absolute Alcohol is anhydrous and hygroscopic. Not the nicest sounding pair of words is it? Anhydrous simply means that it is a compound that has had all the water removed. Hygroscopic means that it wants it back! So if you open up a container of Absolute Alcohol, the alcohol will actually soak up some humidity from the air itself. From this you can see it would be useless to go to all the bother of using entrainers and re-distillations to produce absolute alcohol for fuel purposes because as soon as you put it in your fuel tank it would zap some moisture right back out of the air. It wouldn't keep this up indefinitely of course. Actually it would absorb only a small amount. But that is enough to destroy its character of Absolute Alcohol.

9-20 Since alcohol was at one time used widely in car radiators to prevent freezing in the winter, it is apparent that water and some alcohols do mix thoroughly (miscible is the technical word for the complete mixing of two liquids) and that a mixture of alcohol and water has a much lower freezing point than pure water. See Table II for the solubility of alcohols. Thus a tankful of alcohol (Ethanol) with a few percent of water in it would act very nearly as pure Ethanol, which Table II gives a freezing point of 179 degrees F. No danger of freezing except maybe right on top of one of the poles. Even better, this mixture of mostly alcohol and a tiny bit of water will burn the same as 100 percent Ethanol.

9-21 A few percent water in gasoline would be disturbing since gasoline and water do not mix in any proportions normally. Thus in the winter time frozen fuel lines can occur. In the summer the engine would sputter and miss. Neither of these conditions would be a problem with alcohol.

ETHANOL & WATER

9-22 How well will Ethanol and water burn as a fuel? That depends on the amount of water. But for rather large amounts of water it won't hurt a thing. Concentrations of 50 percent water and 50 percent alcohol have been used satisfactorily. This is about the bottom limit. It is interesting that one early investigator recommends this 50-50 ratio to be used in a specially designed engine to produce a pseudo steam-engine. His analysis was that the half alcohol would burn and turn the half water into live steam which would then help move the piston. Who knows, it might work!

9-23 For a variety of reasons, it is best to use higher concentrations of alcohol. 90 to 95 percent seems a good compromise. Certainly we could easily use 75% or 80% alcohol and it would burn quite well. But, as the saying goes "there ain't no free lunch!". If the alcohol is reduced so also is the heat value and, hence, the mileage. It's as simple as that. Using a low concentration of alcohol, say 60 percent for instance, will cut down the gross mileage by 40 percent. A 20 gallon tank of 60 percent Ethanol will really have only 12 gallons of useable fuel. The other 8 gallons is water which is excess baggage and it adds about 64 lbs. of deadweight.

TABLE III

Approximate amount of Heat in a few common fuels

SOLIDS	BTU's per LB		LIQUIDS	BTU's per LB
Wood	07250		Gasoline	18500
Charcoal	13500		Kerosene	
Peat (dried)	07500		Ethanol	1200
Coal	13000			

GASES	ORIGIN	BTU's per CUBIC FOOT
Methanol (natural gas)	drilled from wells as is oil	1100
Coal Gas (methanol, hydrogen)	made by heating coal in air-tight environment	500
Water Gas & Producer Gas (hydrogen, carbon monoxide)	made by passing steam over hot coal	250

One BTU (British Thermal Unit) is the amount of heat required to raise the temperature of one pound of water one degree Fahrenheit.

9-24 So if you are getting 20 miles to the gallon on pure ethanol you will have only a range of about 240 miles with 60% with a 20 gallon tank. Using pure ethanol (or nearly so) the range would be 400 miles. Even with 90 percent ethanol you are carrying two gallons of water around in your full 20 gallon tank.   Besides this the excess water makes it increasingly difficult to start your motor.   Alcohol starts harder than gasoline even in the best of times.

9-25 Remember that with gasoline the refiner can and does add more volatile (easy to evaporate) components in the winter.   This makes it easier to start.   Ethanol is a single compound not an admixture, as is gasoline. It has but one single boiling point (173F/78C degrees) and that is relatively high. About the only real argument for using wetter ethanol than 95 percent is if you are using a still design which is more efficient at some lower value. It is never advisable to go below 75 percent.

9-26 One method of making it easier to start an Ethanol powered motor is to preheat the carburetor air before running it into the cylinders. This is best done electrically and only just prior to starting the motor or while cranking it.

ETHANOL AS A FUEL

9-27 Ethanol has some real advantages as a fuel and some real disadvantages; just like gasoline.   After we run through a quick comparison between gasoline and alcohol it will be easy to see they about balance out--which means that once the dust settles on the research and development, ethanol will be every bit as good as gasoline right across the board. The real question seems to lie in the area of whether alcohol can be made available in sufficient quantities and at a low enough price.

OCTANE

9-28 The octane rating of ethanol is about 100 using the common pump method now widely accepted (by law) in the U.S. Regular gasoline with a lead additive is about 90.   Lead-free blended gas is a little less yet. Thus alcohol can be used with spark engines (common automobile and small tractors) having higher compression ratios than possible with regular gas.

9-29 It is also a good diesel fuel but some lubricant must be added for most diesel engines or you will burn out the fuel injection pump (which was normally lubricated by the oily diesel fuel). This latter problem with diesels is strictly an engineering problem. The ethanol helps the octane rating but, for diesels only, probably not enough to compensate for the extra pump cost.

9-30 Why is octane rating important? Because Horsepower is important. Here is a common formula for horsepower for a single cylinder of a multiple cylinder engine:

$$HORSEPOWER = \frac{PLAN}{66000}$$

P - Pressure in cylinder at explosion
L - Length of the stroke
A - Area of cylinder
N - Number of power strokes per minute

9-31 In other words, if you multiply P times L times A times N and then divide this result by 66000 you will get the horsepower of each cylinder of a multiple cylinder engine.

9-32 Notice that any time you multiply something by a larger number you get a larger result. Thus if we can increase the size of any of the factors P,L,A or N we can directly increase the horsepower of the engine. Increasing L or A simply increases the size of the engine. So if we are trying to get as much horsepower out of as small an engine as possible, we won't even consider this method. N, the number of power strokes per minute can be increased somewhat but there are sharp physical limits beyond which the engine merely throws itself to pieces, which is no fun at all.

9-33 This leaves us only the pressure, P. The pressure can be increased by using different fuels and by squeezing the fuel mixture more before exploding it. We are limited in the fuel we can use to what is readily and easily available in wide distribution. So we are left with squeezing the fuel and air mixture as much as possible before exploding it.

About the time we think we can make ends meet, somebody moves the ends
Herbert Hoover (who should certainly know about those things!)

9-34 Figure 1 shows what we mean by the compression ratio. When the piston is at the bottom of its stroke, the empty space above it is at its largest. When the piston is at the top of its stroke, the empty space is smallest. The ratio (dividing the larger by the smaller) of these two spaces is the compression ratio. For instance if the piston traveled down the cylinder 6 inches on the downward stroke and came up to within 1 inch of the top on its upward stroke, then the exploding gases can expand to 6 times their original volume before being expended from the cylinder. Thus the cylinder has a compression ratio of 6 divided by 1 (6/1) or as it is more commonly written 6:1 or simply stated as "6 to 1". Early engines had compression ratios of 4 and 5 to 1. Modern engines commonly have ratios of 7 or 8 to 1 or thereabouts. In an actual engine it is not as easy to compute the compression ratio because the cylinder head is not perfectly flat and smooth as we have shown in our simplified diagram. But the principle is the same.

Figure 1
COMPRESSION RATION
Diagram greatly simplified. No valves, spark plugs, etc. have been shown

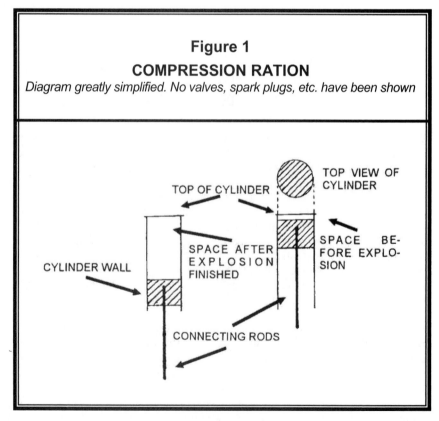

9-35 The reason older cars did not have higher compressions was not that engineers in 1920 did not know about the formula above. They knew it very well. However, low grade gasoline "knocks" or pings at compression ratios higher than 4 or 5 to 1. This is because for smooth power transfer the flame in an exploding cylinder should move smoothly and regularly outward from the spark plug when it is ignited. When a gasoline knocks it indicates that some "detonation" is taking place elsewhere at another place on the cylinder head. This simply means that squeezing the gas so much more tightly in a higher compression engine heats the gas higher and some of it tends to spontaneously combust with or without the spark plug. When this happens, instead of a smooth flame front, two or more separate explosions occur and cause the piston to be knocked sharply to one side or the other (ever so little but still enough so you can hear it "knock" on the cylinder wall).

9-36 This waste power and is hard on the engine. Both the waste and the knock are undesirable. After experimentation it was found that certain of the constituents of gasoline (see Table I) resisted this tendency to pre-ignite more than others. The best of the lot was OCTANE so it is used as a standard for anti-knock ability. Octane was arbitrarily given a value of 100 and all other gasoline and compounds compared to it as less than 100 (poorer) or more than 100 (better).

9-37 During the early 1930's Tetraethyl lead was found to help increase the octane rating of gasoline and it was used for many decades for this purpose and was usually called "Ethyl" or "high test" to distinguish it from "regular" gas. Its use has now been mostly discontinued because of pollutants. Ethylene debromide is another additive that increases octane rating.

9-38 But even these additives have their limitations. To increase the compression ratio much above what is presently used the best solution is to go to diesel where the octane rating of the fuel is immaterial. It is not forced into the cylinder until AFTER the cylinder is at or near the top of its compression stroke. Consequently compression ratios DOUBLE those used in gasoline engines (16:1 and higher) can be and are used for diesel engines.

DIESELS

9-39 Eventually if Ethanol, methanol or some similar replenishable fuel comes into universal service the engine of choice will likely be the diesel. The diesel must be heavier built to withstand the extreme pressures it generates (over 500 lbs. pressure per square inch and 1000 degrees F. temperature at the top of the stroke before ignition) but it is one of the most efficient engines ever built. The science of metallurgy has advanced to the point where relatively light-weight, and strong diesels can now be built. But the cost is still greater than spark plug engines. Also, the diesel performs poorer than gasoline engines at lower speeds and under varying speed conditions.

9-40 These problems are not large. Interestingly enough the diesel engine always takes in the same amount of air on each stroke (contrasted to the adjustable flow of the gasoline engine) so the power of the stroke is varied by varying the amount of fuel inserted. Thus the air to fuel mixture in a diesel can vary from 20:1 or so up to 80:1 or more. In a gasoline engine it is held steady at about 14.5:1, regardless of speed or load conditions. Rudolph Diesel, who invented and developed the diesel in the 1890's, fell overboard in the English Channel and drowned in 1913, at the age of 55.

9-41 Thus while the octane rating of 100 for ethanol is important when dealing with spark-plug ignited engines (commonly called gasoline engines) it can be seen that it will be of little import if diesels evolve as the most fit of the species. And Darwin has already told us what happens to the unfit.

A WINE AND BEER PUZZLE

A wine and beer wholesaler started in business with a number of partly full barrels and kegs of each as shown at right.

He sold $100 of wine to one customer and $100 of beer to another. But he sold the wine for twice as much per gallon as the beer.

When the transaction was ompleted he had only one barrel or keg left.

These are the odd lot contents of each barrel of keg in

How much is that barrel or keg worth?

Answer at end of Chapter 12

9-42 The hard-starting features of ethanol will also be solved by switching to Diesel; all Diesels are hard to start. Let's see, was that really a solution or should we be in politics?

VAPOR LOCK

9-43 It was mentioned previously that hard starting is generally caused by the higher boiling point of ethanol (173 degrees F.). This higher boiling point does have some advantages. Vapor Lock is caused by gasoline turning into vapor (gas) before it is supposed to do so (in the carburetor and intake manifold); particularly on hot summer days. Alcohol, with its much higher boiling point will not vaporize nearly so easy.

9-44 The fuel pumps and associated fuel system in a vehicle is designed to pump a liquid and not a gas. When the vapor comes along into the pump it can wreak havoc with the pumping action. It might stop the action altogether if it is a large bubble of vapor, in which case the vehicle stops dead too. Or, more commonly, smaller bubbles cause the vehicle motor to miss while the fuel pump is trying to disgorge those awful bubbles. Vapor locks usually occur in the hot summer time or if a vehicle has a poorly designed gas line system that routes the line too close to a hot exhaust manifold or muffler system. Ethanol is not prone to vapor locks.

ETHANOL & POLLUTION

9-45 Now we can discuss some very large advantages indeed. First, Ethanol burns cleanly. It carries along some of its own oxygen supply (much like gunpowder which does not need any oxygen from the air). For this and other reasons rockets often are designed using liquid oxygen and an alcohol fuel. Only half as much oxygen is needed as would be needed for petroleum products. This saves weight and weight is all-important to a rocket's performance. But the benefit to us is clean burning. Alcohol burns easily and completely.

9-46 The primary exhaust products coming out of a vehicle using Ethanol fuel are carbon dioxide and water. If these are polluting then we and the entire plant kingdom are in real trouble. There will be other trace products caused by impurities or incomplete combustion but these are few in number and small in quantity.

9-47 Ethanol also is an excellent solvent for many lacquers, gums and resins. Gasoline engines deposit resins in the carburetor and elsewhere through the fuel system. Their carburetors need to be cleaned of this occasionally. Gasoline also coats the inside of the engine with heavy deposits of carbon and other burned byproducts.

Ethanol does none of the above. In fact it actually cleans up a car that has been running on gasoline. Ethanol even cleans up rust from fuel and tank lines. There is a note of caution here. The paint on most vehicles is a lacquer base (some "natural" and some synthetic) paint which may be dissolved by Ethanol. **More precaution may be needed when filling your fuel tank if you wish to protect your shiny new finish.**

9-48 One of the worst - if not THE worst - pollutant in gasoline is sulfur dioxide. There is no sulfur dioxide effluent from an ethanol fueled engine.

9-49 absolute alcohols (100 percent Ethanol) has no corrosive properties. However the commoner 95 percent mixture is slightly corrosive on lead and aluminum. The use of aluminum blocks in Ethanol motors may need some study. Probably a proper alloy of aluminum can be made. On the other hand, the corrosive action may be small enough as to be negligible over the life of the motor; motors don't last very long under the best of circumstances.

ENERGY & EFFICIENCY

9-50 The amount of heat generated by a fuel is measured in BTU's or British Thermal Units. One BTU is the amount of heat required to raise the temperature of one pound of water (16 oz.) one degree Fahrenheit (when the water is at or near its point of maximum density - which is

39.1 degrees F.). In other words if ten pounds of water are raised in temperature by one degree F., then it took 10 BTU's to do this. Conversely, 10 BTU's will raise the temperature of one pound of water by 10 degrees F. For our purposes we can ignore the small deviations that occur if we are not strictly at 39.1F degrees.

9-51 Gasoline will produce about 18,500 BTU's per pound (.45 kg) when burned as compared to 12,000 for Ethanol. (See Table III). This is about 35 percent less or, to put it another way, only 65 percent as much heating value. Since heating value is energy, this would appear to show that alcohol has appreciably less energy. But we aren't through pulling rabbits out of the hat yet!

9-52 The heat value does no one any good if you can't use it. A gasoline burning motor is able to efficiently utilize only about 25 percent of the energy available in the gasoline. No need to go into why here since gasoline is a fast fading fuel anyhow. If you think that is poor efficiency, pity the poor steam engine. Ten percent is not bad for the efficiency of a typical steam engine (90 percent of the input energy is wasted in discarded heat).

9-53 Ethanol, on the other hand, has a thermal efficiency of about 35 percent. Gasohol, by the way, is about 28 percent. Thus the thermal efficiency of Ethanol in a properly designed motor is 1.4 (or 140 percent) times as great as gasoline (.35 / .25 = 1.4). If we multiply the BTU content of both gasoline and ethanol by their respective thermal efficiencies we get their approximate effective heat values

For Gasoline: .25 X 18,500 = 4625
For Ethanol: .35 X 12,000 = 4200
4625/4200 = .9081 or about 91 percent

9-54 Thus ethanol comes within about 91 percent of gasoline as far as power output per pound is concerned. That is close enough to be quite comfortable. These figures all need to be taken as representative only, however. The BTU's in ethanol can be rigorously determined since it is a single well-defined substance (ignoring isomers). Gasoline is a mixture of many compounds and its BTU value is not a single constant and depends on the time and place of measurement--sometimes maybe even the color of the wall in the test room.

9-55 Nevertheless, common values are all close to each other. Further, the efficiency of motors is a very large variable - as one would expect with all of the multifarious designs now extant. But the general conclusions we have reached here are valid: the thermal efficiency of ethanol is greater than gasoline and this helps to make up for the deficiency of BTU's in Ethanol.

9-56 The diesel engine, by the way, has an efficiency of greater than 40 percent when burning diesel or fuel oil (petroleum products). Burning ethanol will not appreciably change this efficiency as it does with the gasoline engine. But if 35 percent is better than 25 percent, then certainly 40 percent rates something more than an honorable mention.

CARBON MONOXIDE

9-57 From an immediate safety point of view, the emission of carbon monoxide is of great concern. A gasoline engine can easily produce anywhere from 5 to 10 percent carbon monoxide (CO) which is, of course toxic to animal life. With Ethanol fuel carbon monoxide is normally not a problem at all. Trace amounts only (far less than one percent) should be the worst expected.

9-58 Carbon monoxide is an odd actor. The hemoglobin in the blood (red blood cells) forms a loose association with the oxygen in the lungs and then acts as the carrier for this oxygen throughout the system. The key word here is the LOOSE association it forms. Loose in this sense means NOT a tight and firm relationship at all. Half the problem with CO2 is because hemoglobin combines with it over 300 times as easily as with oxygen. The other half of the problem is that it combines **PERMANENTLY.** The hemoglobin is lost forever as an oxygen carrying vehicle.

9-59 Oxygen, by contrast, is not strongly attached to hemoglobin. It is very easily given up so it can drop off the train, so to speak, when it arrives at its destination: the cells distributed throughout the body. When both carbon monoxide and oxygen are present, the carbon monoxide is 300 times more likely to be assimilated. And worse yet, once combined the red blood cell cannot be used for oxygen transference any more. Needless to say, if there is much carbon monoxide present the body soon becomes overburdened by the useless red blood cells and the cells of the body start to asphyxiate from oxygen starvation. Death results rapidly even when the concentration of CO_2 is not very great. On the happy side, if the concentration of CO_2 is not very great and the exposure is not long, the body quickly disposes of the neutralized red blood cells and replaces them with new active ones.

SAFETY

9-60 A decidedly large plus for ethanol is that it is safer to handle and store than gasoline. The flash point of gasoline (chapter 3) is about -50/-46C and for ethanol is a little over +50F/10C. Over 100F and 56C degrees difference in flash points indicates a huge safety margin for ethanol.

VEHICLE ALTERATION

9-61 A classic example that is often used to "Prove" the feasibility of alcohol fuels is the Indianapolis 500 mile race held on Memorial Day each year. All of these cars burn pure alcohol (alky). It is hardly the best example around. These cars are all high performance cars and efficiency is the last thing in the world most of them consider. Since efficiency is very nearly our number one ticket item, any comparisons with these vehicles are futile. A better comparison in some respects, is the fact that alcohol makes an excellent rocket fuel. Rocket designers, too, have fuel efficiency as their number one design target. But since most of our vehicles do not use rocket engines, even this comparison falls short of its target. The engines are vastly different. In the long run, ethanol will have to prove itself versus the next best fuel in both performance and availability.

The WHISKEY REBELLION and the NATIONAL WINE COALITION

NO! NO! I'm not the taxman I want to marry your daughter.

Those who do not learn from the past might be the happiest. The Whiskey Rebellion of 1794 is but a footnote of distant history. The National Wine Coalition of 1994 is its natural ancestor. The NWC has learned to fight in the public forums where it can win some and lose some—not on the field of battle where it could only lose ignobly.

THE WHISKEY REBELLION

First, the Whiskey Rebellion which started in 1791 and ended in 1794. We have mentioned this incident before in this book but in a different light. Most of us remember it vaguely as some sort of protest over taxes what concerned whiskey. Actually it was the first EXCISE TAX legislation passed (in 1791) by the new Federal Government in Washington DC. Nowadays it would be called a "sin tax" but in those days drinking whiskey was NOT considered to be a sin.

Transportation of farm products in the United States—or any products for that matter—was difficult in the late 1700s; and the further west the more difficult the travel. You may recall that Horace Greeley admonished the nation "Go west young man, go west."? When he did so he was referring to ERIE, Pennsylvania, NOT Kansas or Nevada or the Pacific Coast.

The whiskey tax caused so much commotion in western areas of the country because much of their corn was distilled right at the farm where it was grown. If corn grown in western Pennsylvania, for instance, was distilled into whiskey before shipping it east, both its compactness and value were enhanced to a large degree. When shipped, a smaller amount would bring a much larger price. Distilled whiskey was so valuable that barrels of whiskey were often used directly as a medium of exchange.

THE NATIONAL WINE COALITION (NWC)

Excise taxes are those taxes levied on the manufacture, sale or consumption of particular products. Excise taxes were not very important, and certainly not oppressive, until the advent of the Civil War. Unfortunately many new Federal precedents were set in that war which were never repealed or, if they were repealed, were visited again at a later date.

The Special Occupation Tax (SOT) stems from the Civil War and is presently looming as a threat to the alcoholic beverage industries which, ultimately of course, means the beverage consumer. It is a tax on retailers (or anyone else) who produce, serve or sell alcoholic beverages. Until recently the SOT was $24 which is not a burden on even small businesses. In 1987 it was increased to $250—an increase of more than 1000% !.

These and other so-called SIN taxes on alcoholic beverages are closely monitored, resisted and turned back, in many cases, by the NWC—usually in a joint effort with other like-minded groups. The NWC has many other activities of ultimate benefit to the consumer, and producer, of alcoholic beverages.

If you wish to be kept informed about all Federal and State regulations and laws affecting the production of alcohol in the United States you should consider joining the NWC. It publishes a newsletter which tracks all such matters as advertising restrictions, marketing, labeling, health and safety, BATF regulations and current legislation pending in all of these areas.

The membership fee for individual wine enthusiasts is small and you may be interested in finding out what benefits this membership confers on you, the consumer or for GASOHOL production.

The location and numbers for the NWC are:

NATIONAL WINE COALTION

1730 Rhode Island Ave. NW

Suite 402

Washington DC 20036

Phone 202-785-9510

FAX 9402

9-62 The comparison between ethanol and gasoline will get better through the years whenever especially designed motors and vehicles come off the assembly lines. After all we are now expecting ethanol to out-perform gasoline on gasoline's home turf! The home team always does better. Gasoline is burned in an engine that has been designed for gasoline and perfected over a period of almost 100 years. It will be a whole new ball game when ethanol is burned in an engine that has been designed and perfected with ethanol in mind.

9-63 Until that happy day, what are we to do with our present inventory of millions of gasoline motors? Fortunately a good many are built so poorly they won't last long enough to be a burden.

9-64 Meanwhile a good deal of experimentation must be done (and is being done). For the most part the present adjuncts of the engine such as fuel pump, radiator, valves, etc. will work with ethanol as-is without any alterations in their basic structure. The main point of difficulty is the carburetor. Carburetors in older cars before pollution controls and four barrels were relatively simple. There was generally a running jet and an idling jet and little else of any complication. In a pure ethanol system we can largely return to these simpler days since many of these pollution devices can be discarded. Some cannot. For instance, the afterburner for the crankcase will still be needed.

9-65 Resizing the carburetor jets is the most important item to consider. Since each motor has its own carburetor design and since many of them differ widely in appearance and application we cannot begin to discuss all the problems associated with re-engineering these devices. We would need a book many times the size of this entire volume. But some helpful hints can be given. Fortunately the jets need to be larger and not smaller. You can purchase a carburetor book or manual (carburetor repair kits are economical and usually contain a complete blow-up diagram of your carburetor - this could be a wise investment for an experimenter) for the model you have and locate the running jets. Work on them first. They will need to be drilled out (if this is possible on your carburetor) about an extra 30 to 50 percent. Experimentation is needed so start with a small value.

9-66 Find out what size the jets presently are and where they are located. There may be more than one if it is a multi-barreled carburetor. Your carburetor book or specs sheet may give this information. If it does not then find the jet and pass a series of number drills through the hole until you find the one nearest in size. Then either use a micrometer to determine the drill diameter or look it up if you know its number. You

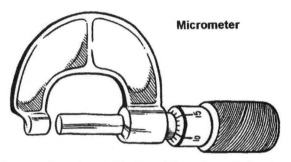

Micrometer

will need a set of number drills (1 to 80) and small fractional drills if you are to touch all bases.

9-67 If you find the jet size is, say, .0520, this will be a number 55 drill. To enlarge it 30 percent means we want to enlarge the area of the tiny jet hole by 30 percent and not the diameter of the drill you will use. It is not the same thing, believe it or not. Since we desire the hole to be 30 percent larger, this is another way of saying we want it to be 1.30 times as large. To increase the size of anything by a certain percentage, we convert the percentage to a decimal and add one. Thirty percent becomes .30 and .30 + 1 is 1.30 or 1.3.

9-68 Thus a 35 percent increase will be a factor of 1.35, etc. To find the value of the new drill, we multiply the old drill size by the square root of 1.3. You may or may not understand why. It doesn't make any difference. Just do it. You don't even need to know what a square root is. Any cheap calculator will do it for you in a jiffy. And it doesn't know what it is either! Thus, using our example of an original jet size of .0520, we get:

For 30 percent increase   .0520 X 1.3 = .0593

For 35 percent increase   .0520 X 1.35 = .0604

etc.   etc.

.0593 is approximately a number 53 drill and .0604 is approximately a number 53 or 54. Remember these are experimental holes so you needn't fret if you can't find the exact size drill you think you need. Use the closest one. Work in this manner little by little trying out each respective size. This means after each prospective enlargement you must reassemble the whole carburetor and try out the engine. The life of a novice genius is not an easy one.

9-69 If the hole is still too small the engine will not run smoothly and may misfire a bit. Remember, it won't run smoothly at slow speeds until you alter the idling jet also. So you have to try the engine at low, medium and high road speeds. If it runs fine, it means the jet size is either right or a trifle large. If too large, it may run fine but it will waste fuel. This is why you creep up on it by drilling slightly larger holes in small increments. You can repeat the whole thing on the idling jets to get a satisfactory low-end performance. Remember that everything we are describing here may be so much useless information for your own carburetor. But the procedure of attack will be the same.

9-70 Ethanol burns a good deal cooler than gasoline. Your thermostat will regulate the temperature of the water but you may find it more economical to put in a smaller radiator. The motor will take longer to heat up on Ethanol and consequently will run rough longer. Preheating of carburetor air (through the manifold or radiator heat) is recommended when using Ethanol although some system will need to be devised so you do not overdo it. As mentioned before you will need electric heat if you are going to heat the carburetor air before you start the engine. There is no radiator or manifold heat to draw from in a dead cold engine.

9-71 It should be apparent by this time why it is not advisable to produce largely varying degrees of purity of Ethanol if one is considering using the product as a fuel. Different carburetor adjustments would be needed over widely varying percentages of purity. If your fuel is 30 percent water, the orifice in the carburetor jet will need to be larger for a given power output of the motor than if there was only 5 percent water. Some tolerance is quite allowable.

9-72 Notice that no adjustments are necessary when using the 10 percent gasohol mixture. By the same token, no adjustments would be necessary if the purity of the ethanol ranged from 95 percent to 90 percent, for example. But large excursions would require carburetor adjustments. Some methods have been devised to allow a continuous adjustment of the orifice over a limited range from the outside of the carburetor. A number of experimenters have also devised their carburetors with easily changeable jets so they can switch back and forth from gasoline to ethanol.

9-73 Another method utilizes a small tank of gasoline (perhaps one or two gallons) in conjunction with the large ethanol tank. This is an advantage for starting purposes. The motor is switched over to gasoline to start it and then switched back to ethanol once it is running. The number of the variations is endless but this should give the novice experimenter some food for thought - or should we say fuel for thinking?

LEGALITIES

9-74 As we have written before, it is illegal for individuals to distill ethanol in any quantities - even a drop! You can legally FERMENT 100 gallons per year per adult for beverage purposes. You do not need a permit and you pay no tax on it. But 200 gallons (100 gallons each for man and wife) of fermented wine or beer will not produce enough wash to distill for very long. Not much pure ethanol will result from the distillation.

9-75 Since any serious experimenter will eventually need to ferment hundreds (and perhaps thousands) of gallons and will need to try out several, if not many, many still designs, it is obvious that for progress to take place either the law will be broken or some accommodation by the authorities must be made.

9-76 Authorities, by their vary nature, do not make many accommodations to suit the needs of individual citizens. But for large groups of citizens accommodations are easily arranged! After the petroleum situation became quite critical and a matter of national peril (and not until!) the government commenced issuing variances to the law for experimenters. A variance is a legal maneuver to actually set aside the law for certain officially approved activities that are large enough to warrant attention but not large enough to justify rewriting the statutes. The first variances issued in the early and middle 1970's were good for experimentation and expired in two years.

9-77 Unfortunately the variance for alcohol distillation will require that you give a lot of nonsense answers to a lot of nonsense questions. But this is to be expected and there is no need to get in a ferment about it. Don't blame the bureaucrats. They have to answer to Congress. To obtain a variance you need to write to your Regional Director of the Bureau of Alcohol, Tobacco and Firearms (BATF or sometimes simply ATF). Their names and addresses are listed in Chapter 12. A sample letter is listed in Chapter 12 also. You can copy this letter or write a similar one of your own. But the points mentioned in the letter should be included in your own letter. If the BATF needs further information they will write and let you know. They will not be fast but they won't be all that slow either. Expect your answer within 30 days unless they are backlogged. We have always found them to be courteous and helpful.

"According to my calculations, if we simply burn it there's enough energy there to last til the next ice age is over!"

Chapter 10:
Medium Scale Production of Ethanol

FERMENTATION FOR
ETHANOL FUEL PRODUCTION

10-1 Fermentation was discussed in Chapter 4 in regards to beverage production. We will re-discuss some of these items in view of the fact that we are no longer concerned about food-grade quality and are now interested in rather large scales of production.

10-2 Even though we are no longer concerned with food grade quality, this does not mean we can throw cleanliness and good practices out the window. Yeast has their natural enemies also. If such things as normally clean containers, proper pH values, proper nutrients, etc. are not provided, we stand a good chance of ruining a batch of mash. Since we are talking about relatively large batches, we cannot afford to let this happen. But we no longer need to worry unduly about whether some of our mash or wash comes into close contact with a little aluminum or iron or lead. We need have no concern whether the containers we are using are those we would not eat from (a large clean wooden through or cleaned steel oil drum for instance).

10-3 The larger scale of production brings up different problems. We will be discussing the operation of a distillation column in a continuous manner in a later section. This is so that it can be kept running at optimum efficiency. It is not so easy to keep a fermentation running on a continuous basis. A mash is usually fermented until the end point is reached. Or the mash can be fermented most of the way and then transferred to another "finishing" kettle while the next batch is brought in and started. This is not always desirable but is sometimes used.

10-4 In previous chapters we recommended as much as a week or two to ferment the mash out completely. Now we are interested in speed and efficiency of the fermentation. Consequently we will expect the fermentation to be over and done within a few days time. With the right nutrients, temperature, yeasts and mash, it can be done in a day.

10-5 Of course, we are no longer interested in necessarily having a high alcoholic content in the wash. What we want is to have a very high fermentation efficiency (little or no starch and sugar left in the wash). We don't care if it is only 10 or 12 percent alcohol or thereabouts so long as all the starch and sugar have been fermented out. We are going to be running it through a still anyhow. so we can use a more dilute mash if it suits our purposes and speeds things up. Of course we don't want to carry this to such an extreme that it requires a lot more heat in the still (boiling off all that excess water) or we trade off a good thing for a bad thing and come out short or even-up. We want to come out ahead. pH is a measure of the ACIDITY or BASENESS of any liquid. 1 is fantastically ACID and 14 is fantastically BASE while 7, in the middle, is perfectly neutral. Ordinary rainwater is about 7 if the air is very clear. There are many easy ways to measure PH (strips of colored paper, pH meters etc) and you should purchase some one or the other of these at a hardware or Home Wine specialty store.

10-6 The pH of the mash should be about 5.4. In any event, the pH should be above 4 and usually between 5.25 and 5.5. The starches and complex sugars will be broken down to simple sugars before introducing the yeast. Remember, yeast can only use simple sugars for food.

10-7 Bulk mash will many times be produced directly from farm products. Table I gives a list of a few common farm products within selected farm products a breakdown of their energy components. We are interested in those that can easily or fairly easily be broken down into

pH

pH is a measure of the ACIDITY or BASENESS of any liquid. 1 is fantastically ACID and 14 is fantastically BASE while 7, in the middle, is perfectly neutral. Ordinary rainwater is about 7 if the air is very clear. There are many easy ways to measure PH (strips of colored paper, pH meters etc) and you should purchase some one of the other of these at a hardware or Home Wine specialty store. *Answer at end of Chapter 12*

TABLE I

Approximate Percent Major Constituents
in selected farm products

Product	Water	Protein	Fat	Sugar Starch	Cellulose	Acid Content
Potatoes	80	2.1	.1	17.2	.5	.5
Soybeans	10	24	18	29	5	____
Barley	12	9	1.4	75	1	.1
Com Flour	12	8	3	75	1	____
Rye	11	10	1	77	.5	____
Wheat	12	13	2	69	2	____
Rice	12	7.5	2	77	1	____

NOTE: These will NOT total 100 percent since small things such as vitamins, minerals, etc. are ignored

simple sugars.   There are many, many excellent fruits, grains & vegetables that are not listed.   Avoid anything with a high content of protein, fats & cellulose.   Look for those with a high content of **SUGARS & STARCHES.**

10-8 Potatoes, Barley, Corn, Rye, Wheat and Rice all satisfy these requirements to a greater or lesser extent.   Soybean was included in the list to give a representative member that does not qualify.   It has too much protein which is a little more difficult to efficiently convert to sugar.   Potatoes have a lot of water, which is a minor disadvantage, but much of the remainder is starch.   Table I lists only a few of the many good candidates for mashing & fermentation.

10-9 To ferment out these materials, enzymes must be added to break down the starches.   These enzymes can be purchased from companies such as Independent Laboratories or Home Wine Retail stores (in some cases).   Addresses for these are in the appendix.   In a great many cases, you can make the proper enzymes yourself by malting one of the grains. Barley is the commonest, but corn and other grains can be used.

10-10 The malting and mashing process is given in Chapter 4. For grains such as corn, the optimum mashing time and temperature is 45 to 60 minutes at 145F/63C. About 5.5 gallons of Ethanol can theoretically be produced from a bushel of corn. But this is like EPA gas mileage - don't expect it! After the fermentation is over, the residue makes an excellent high protein cattle feed and is commonly called DDGS (Distillers, Dried Grain & Solubles). It is a valuable and rich cattle feed. DDGS is usually fed as a supplement to regular feeding rather than as a food all by itself.

10-11 You can malt all of your grain to be converted or you can malt only 10 to 25 percent and add this to the unmalted grain during the mashing process. The latter method gives a higher yield of ethanol. If you make your own malt, set it aside and boil the starchy mash (corn, wheat, etc.) vigorously to break down and separate the starch from the fibers. Then let it cool to about 145F/63C before adding the prepared malt and going through the hour or so of mashing. Check it with an iodine solution, as outlined in chapter 4, during mashing to determine when it is properly converted to sugar.

10-12 After it is converted let it cool to room temperature (below 85F/29C) before pitching the yeast. Add any nutrients deemed necessary (such as B vitamins which are very good) and keep the mixture warm but below about 90F/32C. The activity level of the froth should give you a good idea when it is finished. You can draw off some of the liquid on top and check it with a hydrometer. This will not give you an exact indication of when it is done, but when the hydrometer reading drops to 0 specific gravity, or perhaps a little below, you can assume your mash is all fermented out and ready to distill.

GROWING YOUR YEAST

10-13 Good quality brewing yeasts can be purchased from any Home Wine Retail Outlet or mail order store. Failing this, you can use baker's yeast with satisfactory results. A good brewing yeast should brew quicker and cleaner however, making it easier to distill. Brewer's yeast usually comes in 5 gram packets. 5 grams is about a teaspoonful. However, yeast is much like corn or wheat. One handful of corn is enough to seed the entire state of Iowa or every state in the United States if you are willing to wait enough generations to build the crop up. Fortunately yeast generations only take minutes and hours rather than years and years. Although one packet of yeast is enough to grow your

---

PITCHING YEAST - *a brewers term for adding yeast*

own from, it is foolish not to keep a good ample fresh supply on hand. You do not want to stretch out one packet too far or contamination can creep in.

Figure 1:

PREPARING A STARTER YEAST BATCH

12 oz. orange juice at about 80 degrees F.	**add tablespoon sugar, stir well to dissolve**	**add teaspoon of yeast & stir well**	**cover lightly & leave overnight in warm spot**

After vigorous frothing has commenced add 12 more oz.'s of your malted mash & one teaspoon of sugar, stir well again

After vigorous frothing has set in (about 12 hours) the yeast is ready to pitch

10-14 Here is a variation on an orange juice high powered yeast starter as discussed previously. Take a 12oz/350cc glass of orange juice made from frozen concentrate (make it extra strong) and add a tablespoonful (three teaspoons or 15 grams) of common sugar. Stir it well to dissolve the sugar, heat it to about 80F/27C and add the packet of yeast (about 1 teaspoon). Stir very well again. Cover lightly and leave it in a warm (but not hot) place overnight. Better put the orange juice in a larger container than the glass or it will froth and spill all over the place. Maybe a small saucepan.

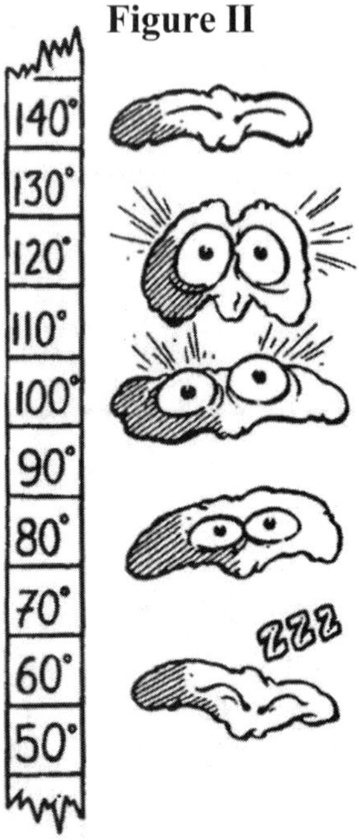

10-15 In the morning there will be froth and other signs of activity. Your yeast has multiplied many thousands of times overnight and you now have a healthy growing colony. Now take 12 ounces of the mash that is ready to ferment, making sure it is nice and warm, but NOT over 85F/29C and put it in the pan with the yeast. Add about one TEASPOON (NOT tablespoon) or 5 grams of SUGAR, stir it well, and leave again overnight.

Figure II

10-16 The next morning it should be working away vigorously again. If it is not then your mash is bad: do not use it. There is very little likelihood of bad mash if you did your mashing and malting correctly. When the yeast starter is working vigorously it is ready to pitch into the mash. You will have about 24 ounces or 700 cc of good active yeast solution. If you are intending to keep this yeast generation going, then remove about 4 ounces or 100 cc and put it in another glass or pan and start the process all over again.

10-17 Don't do this too many times before you start fresh again. The yeast colonies may change with succeeding generations (just as we all do) and you may eventually end up with a colony that is either contaminated or does not convert sugar to ethanol efficiently. The yeast starter you have made is easily ample to start a barrel (50 gallons or 190 liters) of mash. If your batch is larger than this, then start out with a little larger proportions of everything (except the yeast) in your starter batch. A good rule of thumb is to use at least a quart/liter of good vigorous starter batch for each 100 gallons or 400 liters of mash.

10-18 As you may have surmised by this time the act of putting the yeast into the mash is called PITCHING the yeast. Pitch the yeast colony (called a yeast starter batch) and then mix the mash vigorously with a wooden paddle or whatever. Within a few hours you will notice the fermenting activity. With healthy yeast and a well-prepared starter in a good mash, the ferment can be over in as little as 8 to 10 hours. More likely, though, it will be at least two days and maybe three or four.

10-19 For every pound of sugar in your mash, you will theoretically get about 1/2 pound each of Ethanol and Carbon Dioxide (CO_2). In small operations, the CO_2 is simply bubbled off into the air. However if you have a large batch going, a lot of carbon dioxide will be given off. You may want to devise a means to capture this and solidify it into dry ice. But do this only if you can locate a ready and profitable market for it. The stuff doesn't freeze at decent temperatures like ice. Try maybe - 100F/-73C or thereabouts!! Packers and shippers are several good candidates for customers.

EXPERIMENTING PRODUCES EXPERTISE

10-20 Do not start off the first batch you make on a large scale. Start off with a gallon or two and gain some expertise. Experiment until you feel quite competent with your methods and materials. Then, and only then, gradually increase the size of your batches until you are up to working scale. That is, unless you have ample money to throw down the drain ....which is where bad batches go!!

PREPARATION FOR DISTILLING

10-21 When the mash is through fermenting it is ready to be used as a wash in your still. Let it settle out as much as possible and then siphon or otherwise remove the liquid from the spent grains as far as possible. Let set another day to settle and once again siphon, ladle or otherwise pour off the top liquid. It would be good to devise a coarse filter that is easy to reclean. Much time will be saved. Instead of wasting a few days waiting for the lees or residue to settle, you could merely send the mash through your filter and put it in the still directly afterwards. A very fine metal screen will work. If it is too fine it will clog immediately and forever need cleaning. If it is too coarse, it will leave so much residue that your still will soon get plugged up. A superior solution is to have several grades of screens that are used one after the other or in some simultaneous combination. There are a number of companies that manufacture ready-to-use filters of various sizes and grades.

10-22 In any event, once the bulk of the solids have been removed, the wash is ready to put into the still and should be done so immediately. It is best not to let any fermented washes sit around for very long. Unless they are very high in alcohol content, they tend to succumb to such things as vinegar bacteria. There are also spores, algae, etc. which find your wash a perfect home. Once you have distilled out the ethanol it is a natural preservative itself. Practically nothing will disturb it in the 90 to 95 percent state - except evaporation. Keep it tightly sealed.

DISTILLATION OF ETHANOL
FOR FUEL PRODUCTION

10-23 In Chapters 4 and 5 we discussed fermenting and distilling in some detail. It seems reasonable to suppose that the same theory would apply when making ethanol for fuel. It does. But, because the final product is to be used for fuel and not as a beverage there are some economies that can be effected. Further, the scale of production will necessarily be larger. Your car can consume more ethanol in a day than you could drink in a year! If you are going to satisfy its thirst you will need to build much larger stills. Although the basic theory is the same for any size still, the practical aspects are not necessarily the same.

10-24 Of course such things as pressure cookers on the stove and using marbles in the reflux column are out. You can now use any reasonable type of material for your still and for the condensing coils. Even a car radiator can be used for condensing (you CANNOT use a car radiator for condensing alcohol which is meant to be drunk). For experimental models almost any type of metal can be used. When a good working prototype evolves, it is wise to replace all the major components with stainless steel or an equivalent non-corrosive, non-poisonous metal. In spite of its name, stainless steel will corrode, but the corrosion is small and so slow the extra investment needed to pay for it is well spent. It will last and last and requires little if any maintenance. While stainless steel is not required for cleanliness its great value in low maintenance

---

The older I grow the more I distrust the doctrine that age brings wisdom.

H.L. Mencken born 1880

and ease of usage will soon pay for itself many times over. It is actually cheaper in the long run than most any of the seemingly cheaper alternatives you may use in your prototype.

CONTINUOUS DISTILLATION

10-25 For large scale production, it is much desired to have your still running continuously rather than in intermittent batches. The pressure cooker method is a good example of a batch process. The system has to be stopped, cleaned, loaded and, worse yet, reheated. The fraction column illustrated in Chapter 5 is a good example of a continuous run still. This will be the model used as an example for ethanol production on a large scale.

10-26 All of the essential details have been given. A large, solid metal cylindrical shell capable of withstanding moderate pressure is needed, first and foremost. This will form the column itself. It can be anywhere from six inches in diameter up to several feet in diameter. The length (height) of the column should be anywhere from 20 to 40 times the diameter. Figure 2 gives the method of computing the volume of a tank in gallons. If it is a cylindrical tank you need know only the diameter and length (or height depending on your view point.

BUILDING A FRACTIONATING COLUMN

10-27 *Because of the number of dimensions and measurements to be used in the following discussion all the units will be kept consistent. It is easy enough to convert these to any other consistent system, such as the metric. Since these were originally formulated for use in America (the U.S.A part of it anyhow) they are in the inconsistent units used in the United States. Sorry.*

10-28 A rough rule of thumb for the column size (for medium size columns) is 8 to 10 gallons of column capacity for each one gallon of ethanol you wish to produce per hour. For instance if you choose a one foot diameter tank that is 25 feet long, you might be able to realize about 18 gallons per hour IF everything is properly designed and balanced.

Figure 3:

SEPARATING THE DISTILLATION INTO STAGES

ONE STAGE

TWO STAGES

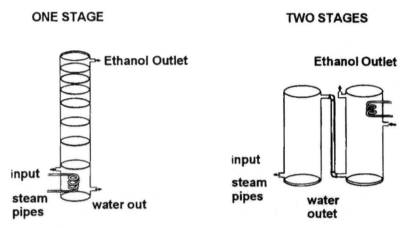

This keeps the hardware from being too bulky and clumsy to properly manage & maintain.

(Tank capacity = v = 5.88D^2
H=5.88 X 1 X 25 = 147 gallons 147/8 = 18.375 or
about 18 gallons per hour of 90-95 percent ethanol).

That is a large IF. For your design you may find that there is an optimum length to diameter ratio.

10-29 A 40 foot tank, 3 feet in diameter gives a projected flow rate of:

$$V=5.88 \ X \ 3^2 \ X \ 40 = 5.88 \ X \ 9 \ X \ 40 = 2117 \ gallons$$

2117/8 = 265 gallons per hour of Ethanol.

Of course this means a gosh-awful amount of wash *(also called mash or beer by various writers)* would be fed into this creature to keep it running continuously.

10-30 It is clear that the large size of the column needed can create some difficult technical problems. If it is built outdoors or indoors it will have to be well insulated or it will be so inefficient as to be worthless. Whether it is inside or out it is going to weigh a bit. A concrete pad will need to be built under it to withstand the weight. A heat delivery system will need to be supplied. Steam pipes into the bottom of the tank are one solution to introduce easily controllable heat with a minimum loss. In the next chapter we will discuss some ways of furnishing heat to make this steam.

10-31 One popular method of avoiding the huge size of a single structure is to break the tank down into several smaller tanks and then connect the top of each tank to the bottom of the next one. Naturally the connecting link needs to be well insulated so there is no appreciable heat loss during this transfer. The internal baffle plates are usually constructed closer and closer together as the top of the cylinder is approached. Figure 3 shows some examples of this.

BAFFLE PLATES

10-32 The construction of the baffle plates will require some care and work. Each plate should have at least three or four holes drilled in it. The holes should not be too large or the distilling action will be reduced. On the other hand if they are too small the still will clog and need cleaning oftener. No larger than 1/2 inch and no smaller than 1/4 inch is a good rule of thumb. Make sure that each plate has at least five percent of its area in holes. Here is a handy formula to determine how many holes you need for five percent holes in any diameter plate:

$$N = .05 \; (D \, /d)^2$$

Where D = Diameter of plate in inches

d = Diameter of holes in inches

N = Number of holes needed

For instance if you have a 12 inch diameter column (one foot) and you want to drill 3/8 inch holes, then the number you will need for five percent holes is:

NOTE: 3/8 = .375

N = .05 (D /d)² = .05 (12/.375)² = .05 (1024) = 51.2 or 51 holes.

This simple formula can be used for any percentage of holes simply by changing the percent you want to a decimal and use it as the multiplier in place of the .05 we have in our formula (for 5 percent). Thus for 9 percent holes of 1/2 inch diameter in an 18 inch baffle plate, the formula would be:

N = .09 (D /d)² = .09 (18/.5)² = .09 (1296) = 116.64 or about 117   holes.

10-33 Notice on page 69 that the small upward pipes for the vapor have a little metal roof on them similar to the common cover used over vent pipes on the roof of your house. Only these, of course, are smaller in size. These "roofs" help trap and condense the water vapors. Notice also that there is a small standpipe leading downward and irregularly placed to bleed off the condensed water to the next lower level. As the Ethanol vaporizes upward we wish the water to condense downward. The water is removed at an appropriate point under the input wash feed point. In some designs a small amount of the final alcohol is fed back down through the system again at or near the midpoint. Apparently this has a regenerative effect such as feedback in an electronic circuit.

BUILDING A CONDENSER

10-34 As mentioned before, a car radiator (or several radiators) can be used for cooling. The water / ethanol mixture has a slight amount of corrosive action on lead and aluminum. One or the other or both of these metals will usually be found in most radiators. The corrosive action is very tiny so very little lead will likely get into your ethanol. Another solution for cooling a large production output is to immerse some very long copper tubing (or other malleable metal) wound in a compact form into a bath of freely flowing cool water. The water is pumped over a small evaporative cooler which uses felt or similar pads to cool the water. The water is cooled by its own evaporation. The cool water is returned to the condenser on the still for re-use. See Figure 4. Evaporative coolers are common in the southwest U.S. and ample literature on their construction can be found in most libraries.

CONSTRUCTION PROBLEMS

10-35 Another problem arises in the construction of the tanks to be used for the column. How will you get all of those metal plates inside and build all of the many, many small standpipes, covers, return tubes for the water, etc.?

10-36 This is where ingenuity comes into play. Everybody has their own solution and there are many clever ones floating around. A suggested method is shown in figure 5. Simply cut the tank right down the middle with a hacksaw (single ended so you can get inside the tank with it) or let your local machine shop do it. You can't use a welding torch as it will leave such a rough edge you will probably never be able to get it to seal back together again - which must be done. File the edges smooth, install hinges, and find a good rubber gasket to fit along the edge to form a seal when the door is closed. The seal material must be able to withstand temperatures up to at least 250F/121C, which is not all that bad.

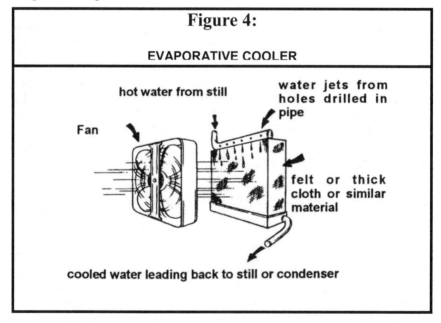

Figure 4:

EVAPORATIVE COOLER

hot water from still

water jets from holes drilled in pipe

Fan

felt or thick cloth or similar material

cooled water leading back to still or condenser

10-37 Of course the door will need a solid clasp, or several clasps, to hold it securely shut when using. The seals need to be good but they do not have to withstand heavy pressures. The pressure inside will be greater than atmospheric pressure, but not much greater.

Figure 5:

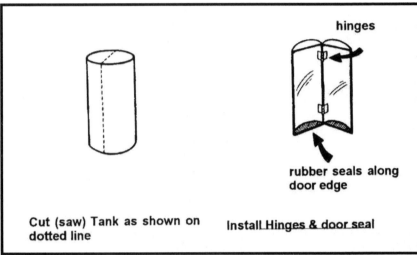

hinges

rubber seals along
door edge

Cut (saw) Tank as shown on
dotted line

Install Hinges & door seal

Once this is done you can now construct baffles inside to your heart's content. They can be welded into the inside of the back part of the tank and rubber seals put on the outside half so they will seal against the door when it closes. Remember that seals inside the tank, between baffles etc, need not be perfect. A good close fit is fine. Nothing needs to be watertight because water and vapor will be travelling up and down the column through all of its many holes and compartments anyhow.

BUILDING A PROTOTYPE

10-38 Before you go to all of the work of constructing a large tank in final detail (or large ANYTHING. for that matter) put together a smaller prototype BUILT TO SCALE and experiment with it to get a good design. THEN, perhaps, build a full size prototype - making all the proper modifications. You needn't take the pains with the prototype which you will eventually bestow on your working model. Make it good but not great. After you have this scale model debugged and working satisfactorily, you are ready to start building the final working model and incorporating all of the improvements you have discovered from your first two prototypes. It is a lot of work but it is very hard to describe that delicious ecstatic feeling that follows the first successful run of the final model. The first successful run may actually be the 5th trial run after debugging!. In Chapter 12 we have listed some reference sources that can be of help to you.

OPERATING THE STILL

10-39 Along the length of your column you should have at least three or four thermometers and-or pressure gauges. Since the volume inside the tank is constant the pressure is proportional to the temperature. What this means is that you should only need a battery of thermometers to give you a good idea of what is going is on. Thermometers are cheaper than pressure gauges. The readings on the thermometers should start at somewhat above the boiling point of water at the lowest point on the tank an decrease to the boiling point of ethanol at the other end of th column (top end).

10-40 If four or five thermometers are carefully placed along the length of the column they should gradually read lower and lower values up the column. For instance when the column is operating at a steady rate, the lowest thermometer (below the level of the wash input) might read 215F/102C at sea level. Each thermometer upward from this point should read lower on the scale. At a temperature of 220F/104C the pressure above atmospheric is only about 3 pounds so a considerable safety factor remains.

10-41 If one thermometer should start reading higher than either of those around it (a hot spot) it means you have a plugged plate at that point. If you avoid putting solids through your still this is unlikely but it can occur. You will need to shut down the operation and clean it out. This a is a good argument for keeping all solids out of the still. Only liquid wash should be allowed to go through it. Even then you can get a lot of foam from proteins and other undesirables.

10-42 For an extra safety factor, you can weld a standard pipe fitting into the top of the tank (or each tank) and install an economical pressure release valve sold for hot water tanks. Buy one with an adjustable setting and set it as low as it will go.

ADJUSTING THE TEMPERATURE & FLOW RATE

10-43 You can vary the temperature up and down the still for optimum operation by several methods. One way is the obvious one of increasing and decreasing the heat supply. Another equally good one is to regulate the flow of the wash into the still. Increasing the flow of wash will drop the internal temperature and decreasing the flow will cause the internal temperature to rise. For a continuously operating still you will eventually have to determine the rate of continuous flow of wash that keeps the temperature gradient in the ranges we have discussed.

10-44 The water residue from the bottom of the column is distilled also, recall, and therefore can be used where distilled water is required. This includes wet-acid batteries and steam irons. However a bad feature is that if the water is very hard in your area (high mineral content such as limestone) the inside of the column will tend to become clogged with scale and deposits from the minerals in the water. The design of the still should allow for this eventuality and provide methods to minimize such deposits and or clean them out if if does occur. One way of minimizing these would be to use the residue water from the first wash through as part of the water used to ferment out following batches. By so doing you would not re-introduce a large fresh supply of minerals with each new batch from the fermenter.

ENERGY INPUT & ENERGY LOSSES

10-45 In the first rush of excitement over GASOHOL, many experimenters tried using solar energy as a distillation heat source. It will work. One method is to use a large rectangular box placed at an angle to the sun. Figure 6 shows the construction. The box is sealed. The top is covered with clear plexiglass facing into the sun. The bottom is painted black to absorb the heat (heat is one form of energy) from the sun's rays. (White reflects heat, black absorbs it). The box is at an angle constantly facing the sun. As the wash slowly comes in the top, the alcohol evaporates from it firsthand then condenses on the cooler plexiglass or glass surface. It runs down this surface into the small catch basin at the bottom and is removed at this point. It is simple enough. Obviously it is inefficient (a lot of water evaporates, too) and show and depends on the sun which is not dependable in some places. But it does work. And it is a good first prototype to work on. This design is by Lance Crombie who has devoted a lot of time and attention to solar stills and ethanol fermentation and distillation. He is one of the pioneers in this modern field.

10-46 Other heat sources include methane (see next chapter), wood, coal, your own ethanol or refuse oil from crankcase drainings. No matter what heat source is used it is important to use as little as possible. In a large scale operation even a small heat loss can add up to terrific inefficiencies over a short period of time. As much time and attention should be given to heating and heat loss as to any other of the major areas of design.

Figure 6:

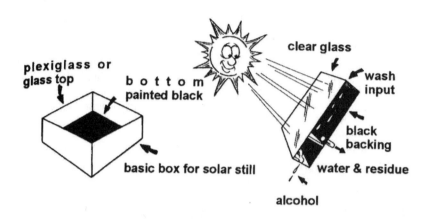

plexiglass or
glass top

bottom
painted black

clear glass

wash
input

black
backing

basic box for solar still

water & residue

alcohol

DENATURANTS & TAXES

10-47 If Ethanol eventually does become a universal fuel being used on the scale gasoline now is, a large battle looms on the horizon. It is difficult to foresee whether the battle will be with bureaucracies, legislatures, private groups, religious groups, none of these, or all of these. This is over the matter of adulterants.

10-48 At present all non-beverage alcohol produced is rigidly controlled. Except for a few special cases. It is required that adulterants (poisons) be added to this alcohol. The philosophy behind such an extreme measure is obvious. If you drink adulterated ethanol to avoid paying the tax, the penalty is death or blindness. In few other areas do we allow such absolute madness to prevail. But since we all grew up with this system it has a way of seeming to be the natural order of things.

10-49 Unfortunately, many of the very institutions in our society that should be appalled and oppose this intentional adulteration (religious groups, civil rights groups, etc.) have their own moral or other axes to grind and acquiesce in this Kafkaesque (gruesome and weird) behavior.

10-50 Continuing this adulterating scheme on a product so widely distributed and used as a basic fuel will result in increasingly large numbers of dead and blind amongst the young, the ignorant and the unwary. As bad as this seems it is not the worst of the picture. The total number of such mishaps probably would not even approach the number of motorists that are annihilated each year (nearly 50,000). We have learned that we can live with these numbers quite comfortably. The real problem is the bureaucracy that will come into existence. The involvement by the government in more detail of our lives will be enormously expanded. New harassment laws with no social benefit (carrying unadulterated fuel, using unadulterated fuel, selling unadulterated fuel, etc.) would be passed. New forms will be devised requiring producers and distributors to hire people to fill them all out and mail them in quadruplicate to Washington D.C. (or your state capital). The user will pay the bill for this in increased prices, lower availability and lost time. It will simply build a large overall national inefficiency factor into the entire fuel situation.

10-51 On the other hand, a tax on Ethanol as a fuel is inevitable. Assessing reasonable taxes to pay for reasonable services is one of the prime functions of government. Without taxes we wouldn't have highways, airports, sewers, running water, and that great feeling of relief on April 16 each year. But we do not need to continue practices that have long outlived their usefulness or need - indeed if there was ever any real need for the adulteration of ethanol.

10-52 Most people are not going to drink ethanol fuel because of the obviously unsanitary (from human standpoint) handling it receives from production through distribution. The taxes lost through beverage taxes will be tiny compared to the huge yield that will result from ethanol fuel taxation.

I swear this book gets bigger every time I open it!

Chapter 11:
More Replenishable Fuels & Topics

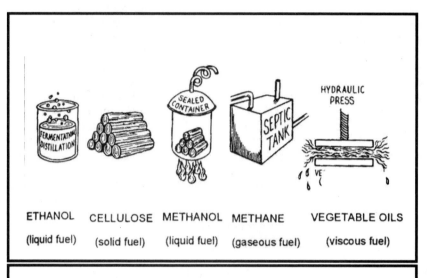

ETHANOL	CELLULOSE	METHANOL	METHANE	VEGETABLE OILS
(liquid fuel)	(solid fuel)	(liquid fuel)	(gaseous fuel)	(viscous fuel)

Some replenishable fuels, showing one of the commonest & easiest

methods of production.

SUNLIGHT

11-1 There are other good replenishable fuels besides those few we have discussed so far. Replenishable fuels derive their energy from the same source we do: the sun. Of course the sun is **NOT** replenishable at all. Right before our very eyes it is burning itself out to extinction. But it is happening so slowly compared to our life spans we find it comforting to declare it replenishable. Furthermore the tiny amount the earth captures from the total radiated and "lost" into space every second of every day of every millennium is so small (about .0000000001 of the total) it is plain to see that if even so small a portion as 1% struck the earth it would be burned to a crisp in the blink of an eye. In the light of these figures it does not stretch credibility to consider sunlight to be replenishable.

11-2 Except for nuclear energy, the sun is the source of all the energy for all the food we consume and all the fuels we burn, including gasoline and coal. The problem with gasoline and coal is not that they are not replenishable, because strictly speaking they are. The problem is that replenishment taxes thousands of years and enormous natural resources for a very low yield. If we can sometime in the future find a way to speed up the process with a greater yield we may return to the use of gasoline. Don't look for it to happen soon.

11-3 Since the sun is the source of all our energy (except nuclear), it would be most efficient if we could convert sunlight directly into whatever work we wished to do. Light a bulb. Turn a motor. Heat a room. This is the direction that a good deal of research is now taking. Solar panels are one result of this research. At the present time we have not been able to come up with any direct method that is economical or efficient enough for general usage.

11-4 However many good indirect ways of utilizing sunlight have resulted. Generators at the bottom of waterfalls are a good example of reclaiming the energy of evaporating water. Wind generators capture the energy caused by uneven heating of the earth's surface. Tidal generators that rise and fall with the tides capture the gravitational energy of the

Figure 1:

Principal Constituents of Foods & Replenishable Fuels

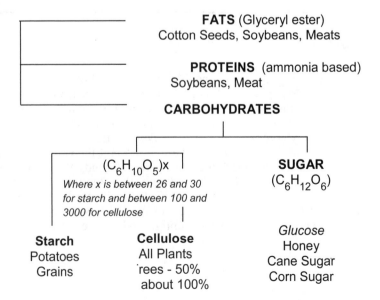

FATS (Glyceryl ester)
Cotton Seeds, Soybeans, Meats

PROTEINS (ammonia based)
Soybeans, Meat

CARBOHYDRATES

$(C_6H_{10}O_5)x$
Where x is between 26 and 30 for starch and between 100 and 3000 for cellulose

SUGAR
$(C_6H_{12}O_6)$

Starch
Potatoes
Grains

Cellulose
All Plants
ˉrees - 50%
about 100%

Glucose
Honey
Cane Sugar
Corn Sugar

sun and the moon (the only exception to the first sentence in this paragraph is that we can harness a small amount of tidal energy from the moon's orbit around the earth).

STORED ENERGY CONVERSIONS

11-5 Better yet, we do have at our disposal a great deal of stored energy from the sun. All the food we eat comes from stored energy. Plants are able to use green chlorophyll to combine carbon dioxide (CO_2), water (H_2O), and air (Oxygen, O_2 and Nitrogen N_2) to store the energy of sunlight. Sunlight, falling on the green leaves, provides the energy to drive this food factory. Whole new groups of compounds are built up by the plants and stored in their tissues or fruits. Most of these new compounds are easily broken back down again with the resultant release of the stored energy of the sun.

11-6 We use many of the compounds as foods. Figure 1 gives a breakdown of the principal constituents of foods. These same products form the basis for almost all of our replenishable fuels. The plants we grow and the foods we eat furnish us with an abundant supply of stored energy from the sun. We have only begun to tap the real potential from this huge natural and replenishable supply. It has been estimated that enough cellulose rots away on the ground each year (straw, old trees, dead weeds etc.) to supply us with more than enough energy to completely replace petroleum products! And that is only the stuff we neglect.

11-7 We have already discussed fermentation and distillation as a very good method of reclaiming some of this energy. Fermentation and distillation give us the energy from sunlight in the form of ethanol. We will now discuss very briefly a few other ways of recapturing the energy of the sun from some of the plant products shown in Figure 1.

CARBOHYDRATES

11-8 Carbohydrates are a Pandora's box. Once we start discussing them all hope of ever being able to say enough is lost. This is not because they are difficult to understand or so terribly complex. On the contrary it is because there is so much about them that is interesting and applicable to our everyday life.

11-9 We have already discussed to some extent two of the three most important carbohydrates. These are sugar and starch. Simple sugars must be present if common yeasts (the commonest strain of yeast for fermenting is **Saccharomyces Cerivisiae**) are to produce alcohol. If starch is present it must be converted to a simple sugar before it can be fermented.

11-10 Enzymes are a "natural" way of changing complex sugars to simple sugars or changing starch to simple sugars. There are also "chemical" ways of doing the same things. We have put natural and chemical in quote marks because there is hardly anything un-natural in this very natural world of ours. If it were un-natural it wouldn't be here. Enzyme action is not well understood by chemists and is likely only a simple chemical (non-living) product of the plant or animal metabolism itself. If all this seems unclear, relax. There are plenty of smart people working on the matter even now while you are reading these words. Perhaps in a few days they will be able to tell us much more about the action of enzymes (and chemicals too!) than they can today. But we (society) know plenty enough to do the job we are undertaking in this section.

11-11 Although we have mentioned two of the common and important carbohydrates, we have said little or nothing about a very, very important third member: Cellulose.

There are other carbohydrates besides sugar, starch and cellulose, but these three constitute the major ones of interest to us

CELLULOSE

11-12 Epimetheus opened the lid to Pandora's box and the only good thing that resulted was "hope". A jolly little bespectacled college professor, Dr. Christian Friedrich Schonbein, peered nearsightedly into his porcelain reaction vessel in Switzerland in 1846 and saw another hope of mankind. The puffy white substance looked like the cotton he started with. But it wasn't. For one thing, when ignited it exploded violently. He had produced nitrocellulose or **CELLULOSE NITRATE**.

11-13 Four huge and totally different industries arose from this humble beginning. The fine polished finish on your car (lacquer) is very likely a product of cellulose. The paper in this book you are reading is cellulose. Vary likely some of the synthetic clothes you are wearing are made from cellulose. A good many of the plastics around you are produced from cellulose. Smokeless powder comes from cellulose. The sponges in your kitchen and the explosives used in the mines are both from cellulose. Is is any wonder that we dread starting on the subject of cellulose? How do you stop? In a standard sized book such as this one, we can only hope to touch the highlights.

METHANOL FROM CELLULOSE

11-14 The easiest way to re-capture sunlight energy in cellulose is to burn it. If you have a large supply of deadwood or trees, you can use this directly to heat your still. However, it is a little difficult to properly regulate heat using wood. It is easier with coal, but still not easy. A way out of this is to produce methanol from the wood by heating it in an air-tight enclosure. When wood (cellulose mixed with a thick tarrish substance called lignin) is heated above its kindling or burning point, while kept from oxygen--so it won't simply burn--a large amount of burnable vapors are released. These vapors do not burn in the hot atmosphere inside the closed container because no outside air (oxygen) is let in. The vapors are then conducted outside through a pipe and cooled by using a normal condenser just as with a still.

11-15 The vapors contain many valuable products but the commonest is **METHANOL** or wood alcohol. It is a liquid at room temperature but readily evaporates (as does ethanol). Table II of Chapter 9 gives its prime characteristics. It can be burned to release heat the same as gasoline and ethanol. It does not have quite the energy of ethanol nor does it mix with gasoline as does ethanol. Methanol sinks to the bottom of the gasoline and stays there. Some chemicals can be added to the mixture to cause them to mix freely (be miscible) but this is generally not worth the time and attention considering some of the other disadvantages of methanol and the easy availability of ethanol.

11-16 Methanol can be mixed with ethanol (don't confuse these two) as a fuel and used wherever ethanol and gasoline are used. Unfortunately it requires a large amount of cellulose to produce sensible amounts of methanol. As with ethanol, the residue of producing methanol is valuable itself. That residue is charcoal, and is used in steel production for a source of fairly pure carbon. It will also produce a good backyard steak if you don't overcook it. In Texas and Oklahoma they don't. Elsewhere you are on your own.

11-17 In our not too distant past, Methanol was produced entirely by heating certain hardwoods (such as birch and beech) in the absence of air. This is how it came to be called Wood Alcohol. However, now it is produced primarily by heating under pressure the two gases, hydrogen and carbon monoxide (both of which are relatively cheap) along with a catalyst such as zinc, oxide or chromium oxide. In spite of its relative cheapness and availability, it is not nearly so available and immediately usable a resource as is ethanol.

11-18 METHANOL is quite toxic. It is chemically altered by the body's chemistry as is Ethanol. However Ethanol is transformed to Acetyldehyde and acetic acid which can then be disposed of by the body so long as they do not accumulate too rapidly. Methanol, on the other hand, converts to Formalehyde and Formic Acid, both of which are very toxic. (Formaldehyde, when dissolved in water, is called Formalin and is used as an embalming fluid--that should give you an idea!).

METHANE

11-19 Methane is another energy source, such as ethanol, which shows great promise for the future. It also is derived from another one of those processes that are simple in theory, like Ethanol, but fraught with complications in practice. We'll discuss only the basics in detail. This will give you ample material to determine whether you are interested in experimenting with methane production and to get you started in the right directions. There are a number of good books on the market which explore this single subject in detail and which the interested entrepreneur or experimenter should purchase for his personal library. One of these is THE DOS AND DON'TS OF METHANE published by RUTAN Press, whose address is in Chapter 12.

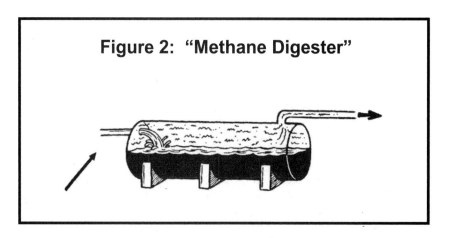

Figure 2: "Methane Digester"

11-20 METHANE is an odorless and colorless gas. It is the prime constituent of both animal and vegetable gases. Any smell associated with these gases is a result of other impurities. Sulphur dioxide, which smells like rotten eggs, is often associated with methane in animal gases.

GAS EXPLOSIONS

11-21 Figure 2 shows a simple methane generator. You need only dump some garbage or sewage in a closed tank, put an exit pipe on the top of it, wait a few days and then start burning the methane gas that comes out of the exit pipe. That is the theory. The practical result, however, is that you may very likely find parts of yourself in the next county after lighting the match to the exiting gas. Methane is not a liquid at normal temperatures. It is a gas.

11-22 This author has only the usual respect for such things as a pail of burning gasoline, for instance. So long as nobody kicks it over, the fire can be put out readily because it burns only on the surface. If you leave it alone it will simply burn itself out, and while this may produce some spectacular flames it can be kept confined and reasonably safe by cool heads and competent handling. Not so with energy in the gaseous state. Make a mistake with methane or hydrogen gas and you will be repaid with an immediate explosion. With gasoline or ethanol, or any liquid fire, it is true that you only have a short while to react as the flames will spread with great rapidity. But this is slow motion compared to an exploding gas. There is no reaction time once the chain is set in motion. This author approaches such bad actors with very great caution. So should you.

11-23 Each gas has an optimum gas to air ratio that produces the best explosion. Best from the point of efficiency, not the hapless observer. Table I shows some limits of flammability (explosions) from some common gases. Where the material is normally a liquid (such as ethanol) the data given is for the vapor of the material.

11-24 Methane is the prime constituent of the natural gas we use in our homes. It should be treated with the same care and attention as natural gas.   Notice that hydrogen is the baddest of the bad for explosions.   It will explode at almost any concentration level. Remember all those movies about the Hindenburg explosion on Thursday, May 6, 1937 in Lakehurst New Jersey? Keep those images clearly in mind when fooling with methane or hydrogen. The maximum explosive force of each gas will be near the upper limits of the figures shown in Table I. Below the lower limit the gas is so sparsely scattered that it cannot continue burning when ignited. It damps itself out. Above the upper limit the gas is so predominant that there is ot enough oxygen available to continue the burning process. It again damps itself out. But within these rather wide limits, watch out.

11-25 In a normal methane system there are a number of ways that explosions can be prevented. Sir Humphrey Davies (1778-1829) was the first to discover that if a gas is passed through a moderately fine wire screen it cannot carry the flame with it. The screen conducts away so

TABLE I

FUEL	EXPLOSION LIMITS	
Methane	5 to 15 percent	*5 to 15 percent methane to air ratio at room temperature and atmospheric pressure.*
Ethanol	3 to 19 percent	
Methanol	7 to 37 percent	
Hydrogen	4 to 74 percent	
Propane	2 to 9 percent	

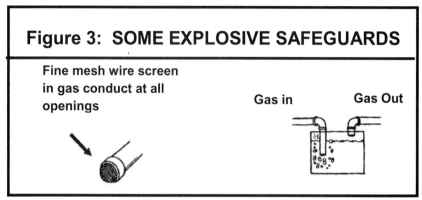

Figure 3: SOME EXPLOSIVE SAFEGUARDS

Fine mesh wire screen
in gas conduct at all
openings

Gas in   Gas Out

much of the heat it is cooled below its flammable threshold and the flame goes out. He built a lantern on this principle (1816) which could be carried into coal mines and yet not create any danger from the pockets of methane gas that exists in all deep coal mines.

11-26 The burning flame was surrounded by a fine metal wire screen, but other than this was out in the open. It is interesting to note that he took out no patent on this valuable contribution to mankind and the grateful coal industry in Great Britain presented him with a complete dinner service of silver plate as a token of its gratitude. So you don't have to pay Sir Humphrey a royalty if you use his idea! Figure 3 shows another explosion dampener. This is a water trap. The water trap does introduce water vapor into the gas however. There are other effective methods also. Using a very small diameter pipe (proportionally) will serve to sap so much heat out of the burning wave front that it cannot be sustained.

RAW MATERIALS

11-27 Almost any raw material which is good food or fuel can be used in a methane digester. The methane is generated by bacteria which are present in the air and in most rotting material. Cellulose will serve as a raw material for a methane digester and this is a valuable way to reduce cellulose. Cellulose is one of the toughest materials to break down into a usable fuel other than burning it in its solid state (trees, etc.).

11-28 Humans and most other animals cannot digest cellulose and it is simply expelled unused in the feces. However sheep, cattle and other "ruminants" (animals with even-toed hooves) can digest cellulose. They are not efficient at it, we might add, which is one reason why cow-chips burn so well--most of the energy remains! But these animals have a special digestive system with several stomachs. They regurgitate their food and chew their cud. They aren't just "dirty" eaters. This is all part of the digestive process. They expel a fair amount of methane gas also. But, at present, nobody has come up with a good idea of how to capture all of this waste methane from grazing cattle.

11-29 Absolutely staggering amounts of methane could be produced by municipal sewage disposals with the installation of methane digesters. Some progress has been made in this area. There are startup costs involved, of course, and there are training problems for operating personnel--and there is a lot of danger. Remember the Hindenburg?

FATS

11-30 Cottonseed and soybeans both provide us with a fair amount of vegetable fats of high quality. Corn does too. There are a number of other vegetables that have a high fat content and there has been much development work directed at finding new such species and increasing the fat yield from the best producers. Fat has twice the energy value, pound for pound, of either proteins or carbohydrates. At present the best bulk fuel producers seem to be in the direction of those we have discussed previously. However vegetable and plant oils may be a valuable source of lubricating and general purpose oils in the future. We have shown in previous chapters why we need not fear the depletion of petroleum reserves so far as FUELS are concerned. It is comforting to know that there are good alternatives for LUBRICANTS also.

SUMMARY OF RECENT
REPLENISHIBLE FUEL DEVELOPMENTS

11-31 A continuous-flow process of converting cellulose to glucose has been developed by two professors at New York University. Professors Brenner and Rugg have developed a converted plastics extrusion machine into a process that converts one ton of old newspapers and sawdust per day into 1200 pounds of glucose. Glucose, of course, can then be directly fermented into Ethanol using procedures we are all familiar with. The developers of this system believe this can cut the cost of manufacturing alcohol in half.

11-32 A scientist from GOODYEAR Tire and Rubber Co. states that it is feasible to produce tires from replenishible alcohols. It now takes seven gallons of oil to make an average tire. Five of these gallons are for raw material and two provide energy to run the plant.

11-33 During the second world war, the U.S. produced over 200,000 tons of butadiene (synthetic rubber) from alcohols. This was half our wartime needs. When petroleum became cheap after the war this was discontinued. The production of Natural Rubber is now very small compared to world needs. This could be changed if the price of other energy-related products continues to rise. 100 percent ethanol is not needed for rubber production. Any grade of ethanol is usable.

I11-34 n the rubber area there is also a small shrub named **GUAYULE** that could be a good answer. Rubber Industry officials are encouraging the government to show farmers how to grow and harvest Guayule. It has been under investigation as a rubber source for more than 50 years and one rubber company (Goodyear again) has no doubts about being able to use the rubber from Guayule if only farmers can learn to properly produce it.

11-35 MILKWEEDS are considered to be a great natural source of natural oils. Dr. Melvin Calvin of the University of California claims that growing oil-yielding plants makes better sense than fermenting relatively expensive grains to make ethanol.

11-36 Brazil is using 20 percent ethanol in its gasohol and claims are made that up to 40 percent can be used without major alterations to the vehicles. They claim that economical catalysts can be used in gasohol to allow the use of inferior grades of ethanol which have a higher water content.

11-37 Approximately 110 billion gallons of gasoline are consumed in the United States each year. This is about 300 million gallons a day or 210,000 gallons a minute. If all of this gasoline was converted to 10 percent gasohol, it would require about 11 billion gallons of ethanol-enough to consume half of the present U.S. Corn crop.

11-38 The U.S. typically produces over 50 million tons of wheat and more than 175 million tons of corn in good years (over 7 billion bushels of corn). Of this corn and wheat crop, over 70 million tons are exported for cash and another smaller amount for International Food Relief programs (free). In the near future the capacity to produce ethanol will be about 50 to 100 million gallons a year - only enough to consume about 25 million bushels of corn.

11-39 Phillips Petroleum Standard Oil of Indiana, and Texaco are amongst a growing number of oil companies - large and small - merchandising gasohol.   At the present time Ethanol costs more per gallon than does gasoline alone.   The 4 cent a gallon federal excise tax on gasoline is exempted on gasohol which helps some.   A few states exempt gasohol from state taxes.

11-40 A gasohol plant design school is located in Kolby, Kansas.

The more you automate a process the more efficient it usually becomes.

Chapter 12:
Charts Tables & References

WORLD CONSUMPTION OF ALCOHOL

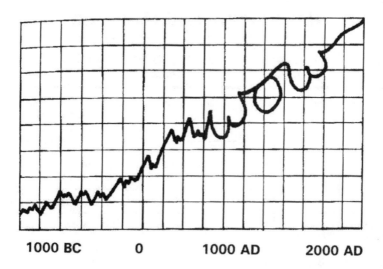

1000 BC   0   1000 AD   2000 AD

12-1 This chapter contains the charts and tables that are necessary to give the reader a complete reference text. They are gathered together in this final chapter to allow for easy referral. A brief explanation is included with those Tables that may not be self-explanatory.

ALCOHOLIC BEVERAGE GUIDE - TABLE A

A quick reference comparison between most common and many uncommon alcoholic drinks . In the column titled "Method of Production" some of the entries state that the beverage was distilled at 160 Proof, or some other proof higher than the final proof at which the drink is served. The simply means that the beverage is "cut" or flavored or diluted in some way after distillation.

ALCOHOLIC BEVERAGE GUIDE

Name	Generic Name	Alcohol %	Proof (U.S.)	Method of Production	Comments
Absinthe	Liqueur	68	136	Compounded	Mixture of aromatic plants and Brandy. Yellow-green, licorice flavored.
Akvavit				Distilled at 190 Proof	From grain or potatoes, flavored with caraway seed and other herbs.
Ale	Beer	6	12	Fermented	Pale to dark; bittersweet.
Alsatian Wine	Wine	14 or less	28 or less	Fermented	Rhinewine; dry white table
American Brandy	Brandy	42 to 54	84 to 108	Distilled at 140 Proof	From wine (fruit or grape), Light gold, oak flavor
Anisette	Liqueur	27	54	Compounded	Flavored with aniseed; white
Angostura	Bitter	40 or less	80 or less	Compounded	Dark, bitter
Apple Jack	Wine	14	28	Fermented	Light, dry
Apricot Liqueur	Liqueur	30	60	Compounded	
Armagnac Brandy	Brandy	42 to 54	84 to 108	Distilled at 140 Proof	Brown, dry, Distilled from
Aromatized Wine	Wine	15 to 20	30 to 40	Brandy Added	
Arrack	Liqueur	30	60	Compounded	Simple syrup, herbs and Batavia Arrack

ALCOHOLIC BEVERAGE GUIDE

Name	Generic Name	Alcohol %	Proof (U.S.)	Method of Production	Comments
Batavia Arrack	Rum	43 to 79	86 to 158	Distilled at 180 Proof	Dry, brandy-like
Beer	Beer	12 to 16	2.4 to 32	Fermented	Fermented mash of malted grains, usually barley with hops added for flavor
Benedictine	Liqueur	30	60	Compounded	Secret blend of herbs and spices. Spicy and sweet, Golden
Bitter	Bitter	40 or less	80 or less	Compounded	Neutral spirits redistilled with or flavored with various herbs and plants
Blackberry Liqueur	Liqueur	43	86		Dark red; sweet
Blackberry Wine	Wine	2 to 8	4 to 16	Fermented	
Bourbon	Whiskey	40 to 55	80 to 110	Distilled at 160 Proof	Made from no less than 51% corn grain
Burgunday	Wine	14 or less	28 or less	Fermented	Red or white. Dry table wine
Brandy	Brandy	42 to 54	84 to 108	Distilled at 140 Proof	From wine
Calvados	Brandy	42 to 54 108	84 to	Distilled at 160 Proof	From apple wine. Brown, dry
Canadian Whiskey	Whiskey	40 to 55	80 to 110	Distilled at 160 Proof	From Rye grains. A blend of Canadian Rye whiskeys.
Champagne	Wine	14 or less	28 or less	Fermented	Sparkling. White or pink, table or dessert, dry or sweet
Chartreuse	Liqueur	43	86	Compounded	Yellow. Sweet, spicy, secret blend.
Chartreuse	Liqueur	55	11	Compounded	Green. Secret blend. Sweet, spicy.

ALCOHOLIC BEVERAGE GUIDE

Name	Generic Name	Alcohol %	Proof (U.S.)	Method of Production	Comments
Chianti	Wine	14 or less	28 or less	Fermented	Dry red table wine
Cider	Wine	2 to 8	4 to 16	Fermented	From apples. Light colored, sweet
Claret	Wine	14 or less	28 or less	Fermented	Red or white table wine
Cognac	Brandy	42 to 54	84 to 108	Distilled at 140 Proof	From fruit wines. Brown, dry
Cointreau	Liqueur	40	80	Compounded	A brand of Triple Sec
Cordial					
Cordial Medoc	Liqueur	30	60	Compounded	Blend of brandy, Curacao Cacao
Creme de Ananas					From Pineapple
Creme de Cacao					From Chocolate & Vanilla
Creme de Cafe					From Coffee
Creme de Cassis		18	36		From red or black currants
Creme de Fraises		30	60		From Strawberries
Creme de Menthe					From Peppermint
Creme de Noyaus					From bitter almond
Cuban Rum	Rum	43 to 79	86 to 158	Distilled at 160 Proof	Light or dark, Sweet or dry
Damerara					Dark Sweet

ALCOHOLIC BEVERAGE GUIDE

Name	Generic Name	Alcohol %	Proof (U.S.)	Method of Production	Comments
Drambuie	Liqueur	30	60	Compounded	Secret blend of Scotch whiskey and honey, Golden, spicy-sweet
Dubonnet	Wine	15 to 20	30 to 40	Fermented Aromatized	Red, sweet appetizer
Forbidden Fruit	Liqueur	30	60	Compounded	From Shaddock grape-fruit & brandy. Orange colr, sweet
Fortified Wine	Wine	16 to 23	32 to 46	Fermented	Brandy added to increase alcohol content
French Vermouth	Wine	15 to 20	30 to 40	Fermented Fortified	Dry white appetizer wine. Brandy added.
Fruit Gin	Gin	43	86	Distilled at 190 Proof	From cereal grains, mostly corn. Sweetened or not, flavored with juniper berries, almonds, cardomons, coriander or licorice. Not aged.
Greek Brandy	Brandy	42 to 54	84 to 108	Distilled at 140 Proof	From fruit juices. Dark, sweet, resinous flavor.
Hollands	Gin	43	86	Distilled at 98 Proof	Dry, white.
Italian Vermouth	Wine	15 to 20	30 to 40	Fermented Fortified	Brown colored. Appetizer sweet or dry. Brandy added
Irish Whiskey	Whiskey	40 to 55	80 to 110	Distilled at 160 Proof	Blend of Irish whiskeys, From barley, oats, wheat and rye.
Jamaican Rum	Rum	43 to 79	86 to 158		Gold colored, sweet
Kirsch	Brandy	42 to 54	84 to 108	Distilled at 140 Proof	From cherries.
Kummel	Liqueur	30 to 40	60 to 80	Compounded	Spiced with caraway and cumin seed.

ALCOHOLIC BEVERAGE GUIDE

Name	Generic Name	Alcohol %	Proof (U.S.)	Method of Production	Comments
Liqueur	Liqueur	18 to 55	36 to 110	Compounded	Various fruits steeped in brandy which then may or not be redistilled. Neutral spirits flavored and artificially colored
Liqueur D'or	Liqueur	43	86	Compounded	Flavored with lemon peel and herbs
Madeira	Wine	16 to 23	32 to 46	Fermented Fortified	Golden dessert. Sweet or dry. Brandy added.
Malaga	Wine	16 to 23	32 to 46	Fermented Fortified	Dard red dessert. Sweet Brandy added.
Malt Whiskey	Whiskey	40 to 55	80 to 110	Distilled at 160 Proof	From not less than 51% malted Barley or Rye
Maraschino	Liqueur	30	60	Compounded	Wild Cherry. White.
Marsala	Wine	16 to 23	32 to 46	Fermented Fortified	Brown. Sweet dessert. Brandy added.
Montilla	Wine	15 to 20	30 to 40	Fermented Aromatized	Straw colored. Dry appetizer wine. Brandy added.
Moselle	Wine	14 or less	28 or less	Fermented	Dry white table wine.
Muscatel	Wine	16 to 23	32 to 46	Fermented Fortified	Golden sweet dessert wine. Brandy added.
Natural Wine	Wine	14 or less	28 or less	Fermented	Non-effervescent (still), or effervescent (sparkling)
Old Tom	Gin	43	86	Distilled at 190 Proof	White, Medium sweet.
Orange Biters	Bitter	40 or less	80 or less	Compounded	Flavored with dried Seville orange peel
Peach	Liqueur	30	60 Liqueur		

ALCOHOLIC BEVERAGE GUIDE

Name	Generic Name	Alcohol %	Proof (U.S.)	Method of Production	Comments
Peach Wine	Wine	2 to 8	4 to 16	Fermented	
Perry	Wine	2 to 8	4 to 16	Fermented	Sparkling. From pear. Straw. Sweet
Port	Wine	16 to 23	32 to	Fermented Fortified	Golden or red. Sweet dessert. Brandy added.
Porter	Beer	6	12	Fermented	Dark, bbitter. Like stout but not as strong.
Pulque	Wine	2 to 8	4 to 16	Fermented	From agave cactus, Resembles sour milk.
Quetsch	Brandy	42 to 54	84 to 108	Distilled at 140 Proof	From plum wine. White, dry
QuinQuina	Wine	15 to 20	30 to 40	Fermented Aromatized	Appetizer. Red or white, sweet or bitter. Brandy added
Rhone	Wine	14 or less	28 or less	Fermented	Red or white. Dry table wine.
Riesling	Wine			Fermented	Dry white table wine
Rum	Rum	43 to 79	86 to 158	Distilled at 160 Proof	From fermented sugar cane molasses. Colored with caramel, flavored with cognac and fruit.
Rye Whiskey	Whiskey	40 to 55	80 to 110		From not less than 51 percent rye grain.
Sake	Wine or Beer	14 to 16	28 to 32	Fermented	From rice. White dry wine beer.
Sauternes	Wine	14 or less	28 or less		Sweet white dessert wine.
Scotch	Whiskey	40 to 55	80 to 110	Distilled at 160 Proof	Blend of straight Scottish whiskeys (made from peat-smoked malted barley)
Sherry	Wine	16 to 23	32 to 46	Fermented Fortified	Amber appetizer. Sweet or dry. Brandy added.

ALCOHOLIC BEVERAGE GUIDE

Name	Generic Name	Alcohol %	Proof (U.S.)	Method of Production	Comments
Silvovitz	Brandy	42 to 54	84 to 108	Distilled at 140 Proof	From Plum wine. Dry, brown
Sloe Gin	Liqueur	18 to 55	36 to 110	Compounded	From wild plum. Red, sweet
Spanish Brandy	Brandy	42 to 54	84 to 108	Distilled at 140 Proof	From Grape wine. Brown, medium dry
Sparkling Asti Spumante	Wine	14 or less	28 or less wine	Fermented	Sparkling. Sweet white table
Sparkling Burgundy					Sparkling. Red or white, Medium sweet table wine
Sparling Moselle					Sparkling White sweet table wine
Sparkling Wines	(see natural wines)				
Still Wines	(see natural wines)				
Stout	Beer	6	12	Fermented	A dark ale. Strong malt flavor. Bitter
Straight Whiskey	Whiskey	40 to 55	80 to 110	Distilled at 160 Proof	From fermented grains and cereals, one of which makes up not less than 51 percent of the grain used...this grain then gives it its name
Strawberry	Wine	2 to 8	4 to 16	Fermented	
Tequila		40 to 55	80 to 110	Distilled	From the juice of the Tequila century plant.
Tokay	Wine	16 to 23	32 to 46	Fermented Fortified	Sweet dessert wine. Red, Brandy added.
Triple Sec	Liqueur	40	80	Compounded	A white, sweet curacao
Vander Hum	Liqueur	35	70	Compounded	From tangerine (mandarines)

ALCOHOLIC BEVERAGE GUIDE

Name	Generic Name	Alcohol %	Proof (U.S.)	Method of Production	Comments
Vodka	Vodka	45 to 57	90 to 115	Distilled at 150 Proof	From a mash of wheat and a little malt. Not flavored or aged. White. Dry.
Wheat Whiskey	Whiskey	40 to 55	80 to 110	Distilled at 160 Proof	From not less than 51 percent wheat grain.
Whiskey					From various cereal grains - can be either straight or blended
Whiskey					Any straight whiskey blended with a neutral spirit, or with another straight whiskey
Wine	Wine	2 to 23	4 to 46	Fermented	Fermented fruits or vege-tables, usually grape. Can be natural (still), sparkling, fortified or aromatized
Zubrovka	Vodka	45 to 57	90 to 115	Distilled at 150 Proof	Vodka flavored with zubrovka grass - slightly bitter. Dry.

WEIGHTS AND MEASURES - Table B

UNITS OF MEASUREMENT

Since this book explains in detail how to **DO** certain things it follows that MEASUREMENTS are needed; for nothing worthwhile can be accomplished in this world without some specifications and limits; both of which require **NUMBERS** and **UNITS**.

Numbers, of course, we recognize and use daily by custom and by agreement.   6 is greater than 2 and 500 divided by 5 is 100.   But numbers used in this manner don't TELL us anything.   If I have 6 apples and you have 2 pears we are beginning to put numbers to good use.   In this case 6 and 2 are the MEASUREMENTS and APPLES and PEARS are the specified UNITS.

Likewise we are familiar with inches, centimeters, gallons, miles, seconds etc. These are all units.

Fortunately some units are shared in common throughout a good share of the civilized world; such units as hours, days and seconds are some of these and teaspoons and tablespoons, although inexact, come close to being others.

Unfortunately not all civilized countries share the same system of units. For instance in the United States, miles, pounds and inches are common units for distance, weight and distance, respectively.   In Canada and Great Britain, as well as in all of Europe and much of the rest of the civilized world, meters, kilometers, grams and such are commonly employed units.   To make matters even worse some of these units are not rigidly defined or are defined differently for different trades in the same country.

In this section we will FIX most useful measurements at their commonly accepted (or legally required in many cases) values.   In most cases these are scientific units but in some cases they have been rounded off or even approximated to give us all a good common basis on which to proceed.

This book was first published in 1973 for distribution in the United States.   Before the end of that decade there were nearly as many copies being sold OUTSIDE the U.S. as inside its borders. Now, a few decades later, it is being sold worldwide.

Consequently in this major revision we have taken great pains to accomodate both of the two major measuring systems in existence.
In the book itself, for the most part, we have given both the METRIC (Centigrade, Meter, Second) system of units and the U.S. (as well as Canadian and British to some extents) system.

Thus a temperature will be indicated as 72F/22C for 72 degrees Fahrenheit or 22 degrees Centigrade. Even though 72F is really 22.22222C, such extreme accuracy is not only NOT needed it is counter-productive. In reality neither the 72 NOR the 22 need be that precise. Often a RANGE is given, such as 72-85F/22-29C, which means between 72 to 85 degrees Fahrenheit which is the same range as 22 to 29 degrees Centigrade.

Mostly these dual measurements will be obvious and the reader will select those that best suits his or her preferences.

In some places where a refinement would be tedious or trivial a single unit, such as the inch or ounce, might be retained. This should cause no problems to diverse readers. A small table is included directly below to reconcile any differences in the text that might still need clarification.

Abbreviations

cm = centimeters
mm = millimeters
oz = ounce
lb = pound
m = meters
kg = kilograms
l = liter
qt = quart
gal=gallon

gm = grams
ft = feet
yd = yard
km = kilometer
F= Fahrenheit
C=Centigrade
cc = cubic centimeter
ci = cubic inch

Some handy equivalents and formulas

1 in = 2.54 cm
12 in = 1 ft
3 ft = 1 yd
10 mm = 1 cm

100 cm = 1 m
1 cc of water = 1 gram
1 ci of water = about 1/2 oz

Some U.S. measure equivalents

1 tablespoon = 3 teaspoons = 1/2 oz = 14 grams
16 tablespoons = 1 cup = 8 oz
4 cups = 1 quart = 32 oz
1 US gallon = 4 quarts = 128 oz
5280 ft = 1 linear mile
640 acres = 1 square mile
1000 meters = 1 kilometer (km) 1000 X 1000 = 1 square km
hectare is the equivalent of the U.S. acre. 1 hectare = (square km)/100 =
10,000 square meters since a square meter is 10.763867 square feet a
hectare is 2.47 or about 2 and a half acres

Some measure equivalents

1 liter = 1000 cc = 2.205 lb
4 liters = 1 metric gallon
1000 meters = 1 kilometer (km)
1 USgallon = 3.79 liters
1 liter = 1.1023 qt
1 qt = .9072 liter
1 oz = 28.4 gm
2.205 lb = 1 kg
1 qt = 2 lb
1 USgal = 8 lb
F = 1.8C + 32
C = (F-32)/1.8
1 pound = 453.592 grams
1 ounce = 28.3495 grams
1 dram = 1.7718 grams
1 grain = 0.0648 gram
1 gallon = 3.785 liters = 3785 cubic centimeters
1 quart = 0.946 liter = 946 cubic centimeters
1 pint = 0.473 liter = 473 cubic centimeters
1 fluid ounce = 0.0295 liter = 29.5 cubic centimeters

MISC.

1 BTU = 252 calories
1 Acre = 43,560 square feet
640 acres = one square mile

TABLE B, below, gives the general relationship between most of the common units of measurement. Using this chart you can find any of the equivalencies of any of the units to each other by either following the top row or left hand column and find the point of intersection in the table.

TABLE B - U.S. LIQUID MEASURE

	Gals.	Qts.	Pts.	Cups	Oz.	T.	tsp.	gr.	lb.
Gallon	1	4	8	16	128	256	768	3785	8
Quart	1/4	1	2	4	32	64	192	907	2
Pint	1/8	1/2	1	2	16	32	96	453	1
Cup	1/16	1/4	1/2	1	8	16	48	225	1/2
Ounce	1/128	1/32	1/16	1/8	1	2	6	28.35	1/16
Table spoon	1/256	1/64	1/32	1/16	1/2	1	3	15	1/32
Tea spoon	1/768	1/192	1/96	1/48	1/6	1/3	1	5	1/96
Gram	.0002	.0011	.0005	.0003	1/28	1/15	1/5	1	1/473
Pound	1/8	½	1	2	16	32	96	473.6	1

PROOF TABLE FOR ALCOHOL - TABLE C

This table gives the relationship existing between the various types
of proof in existence in Great Britain, Canada and the U.S. All of
the various types are referenced to percent alcohol by volume. Note that
both the Canadians and British use the same scale (Sykes) but the
Canadians use 100 proof (Sykes) as their reference point. Anything
UNDER 100 Sykes is UNDER proof. Anything over 100 proof (Sykes)
is OVER proof. Strange huh? The negative signs indicate Under and the
positive signs Over.

% ALCOHOL by volume	PROOF SCALES		
	U.S.A.	British or Sykes	Canadian
2	4	3.5	-96.5
4	8	7.0	-93.0
6	12	10.5	-89.5
8	16	14.0	-86.0
10	20	17.5	-82.5
12	24	21.0	-79.0
14	28	24.5	-75.5
16	32	28.0	-72.0
18	36	31.5	-68.5
20	40	35.0	-65.0
25	50	43.8	-56.2
30	60	52.5	-47.5
35	70	61.3	-38.7
40	80	70.0	-30.0
45	90	78.8	-21.2
50	100	87.5	-12.5
60	120	105.0	+05.0
70	140	122.5	+22.5
80	160	140.0	+40.0
100	200	175.0	+75.0

ALCOHOL CONVERSION TABLE - TABLE D

This table correlates percent by volume to percent by weight and vice-versa. For instance a 12 percent wine (alcohol by volume) would be equivalent to 9.679 by weight.

This table takes into account the shrinkage that results from mixing alcohol with water.

Percentage by Volume   Percentage by Weight

% Vol	Corresp- onding % Weight	% Vol	Corresp- onding % Weight	% Wt.	Corresp- onding % Vol.	% Wt.	Corresp- onding % Vol.
0	0.000	51	43.428	0	0.000	51	58.844
1	0.795	52	44.374	1	1.257	52	59.851
2	1.593	53	45.326	2	2.510	53	60.854
3	2.392	54	46.283	3	3.758	54	61.850
4	3.194	55	47.245	4	5.002	55	62.837
5	3.998	56	48.514	5	6.243	56	63.820
6	4.804	57	49.187	6	7.479	57	64.798
7	5.612	58	50.167	7	8.712	58	65.768
8	6.422	59	51.154	8	9.943	59	66.732
9	7.234	60	52.147	9	11.169	60	67.690
10	8.047	61	53.146	10	12.393	61	68.641
11	8.862	62	54.152	11	13.613	62	69.586
12	9.679	63	55.165	12	14.832	63	70.523
13	10.497	64	56.184	13	16.047	64	71.455
14	11.317	65	57.208	14	17.259	65	72.380
15	12.138	66	58.241	15	18.469	66	73.299
16	12.961	67	59.279	16	19.676	67	74.211
17	13.786	68	60.325	17	20.880	68	75.117
18	14.612	69	61.379	18	22.081	69	76.016
19	15.440	70	62.441	19	23.278	70	76.909
20	16.269	71	63.511	20	24.472	71	77.794
21	17.100	72	64.588	21	25.662	72	78.672
22	17.933	73	65.674	22	26.849	73	79.544
23	18.768	74	66.798	23	28.032	74	80.410
24	19.604	75	67.870	24	29.210	75	81.269
25	20.443	76	68.982	25	30.388	76	82.121
26	21.285	77	70.102	26	31.555	77	82.967

% Vol	Corresp- onding % Weight	% Vol	Corresp- onding % Weight	% Wt.	Corresp- onding % Vol.	% Wt.	Corresp- onding % Vol.
27	22.127	78	71.234	27	32.719	78	83.806
28	22.973	79	72.375	28	33.879	79	84.636
29	23.820	80	73.526	29	35.033	80	85.459
30	24.670	81	74.686	30	36.181	81	86.275
31	25.524	82	75.858	31	37.323	82	87.083
32	26.382	83	77.039	32	38.459	83	87.886
33	27.242	84	78.233	33	39.590	84	88.678
34	28.104	85	79.441	34	40.716	85	89.464
35	28.971	86	80.662	35	41.832	86	90.240
36	29.842	87	81.897	36	42.944	87	91.008
37	30.717	88	83.144	37	40.050	88	91.766
38	31.596	89	84.408	38	45.149	89	92.517
39	32.478	90	85.689	39	46.242	90	93.982
40	33.364	91	86.989	40	47.328	91	93.982
41	34.254	92	88.310	41	48.407	92	94.700
42	35.150	93	89.652	42	49.480	93	95.407
43	36.050	94	91.025	43	50.545	94	96.103
44	36.955	95	92.423	44	51.605	95	96.787
45	37.865	96	93.851	45	52.658	96	97.547
46	38.778	97	95.315	46	53.705	97	98.117
47	39.697	98	96.820	47	54.746	98	98.759
48	40.622	99	98.381	48	55.780	99	99.386
49	41.551	100	100.000	49	56.808	100	100.000
50	42.487			50	57.830		

TEMPERATURE CONVERSION TABLE - TABLE E

This table converts Centigrade degrees to Fahrenheit degrees as this is the usual direction in which you will want to convert. If you can manipulate formulas, the conversion is:

F = 1.8 X C + 32

C = 5/9 X (F - 32)

DEGREES CENTIGRADE TO FAHRENHEIT

°C	°F	°C	°F	°C	°F	°C	°F	°C	°F
-50	-58.0	-23	-9.4	4	39.2	31	87.8	58	136.4
-49	-56.2	-22	-7.6	5	41.0	32	89.6	59	138.2
-48	-54.4	-21	-5.8	6	42.8	33	91.4	60	140.0
-47	-52.6	-20	-4.0	7	44.6	34	93.2	61	141.8
-46	-50.8	-19	-2.2	8	46.4	35	95.0	62	143.6
-45	-49.0	-18	-0.4	9	48.2	36	96.8	63	145.4
-44	-47.2	-17	1.4	10	50.0	37	98.6	64	147.2
-43	-45.4	-16	3.2	11	51.8	38	100.4	65	149.0
-42	-43.6	-15	5.0	12	53.6	39	102.2	66	150.8
-41	-41.8	-14	6.8	13	55.4	40	104.0	67	152.6
-40	-40.0	-13	8.6	14	57.2	41	105.8	68	154.4
-39	-38.2	-12	10.4	15	59.0	42	107.6	69	156.2
-38	-36.4	-11	12.2	16	60.8	43	109.4	70	158.0
-37	-34.6	-10	14.0	17	62.6	44	111.2	71	159.8
-36	-32.8	-9	15.8	18	64.4	45	113.0	72	161.6
-35	-31.0	-8	17.6	19	66.2	46	114.8	73	163.4
-34	-29.2	-7	19.4	20	68.0	47	116.6	74	165.2
-33	-27.4	-6	21.2	21	69.8	48	118.4	75	167.0
-32	-25.6	-5	23.0	22	71.6	49	120.2	76	168.8
-31	-23.8	-4	24.8	23	73.4	50	122.0	77	170.6
-30	-22.0	-3	26.6	24	75.2	51	123.8	78	172.4
-29	-20.2	-2	28.4	25	77.0	52	125.6	79	174.2
-28	-18.4	-1	30.2	26	78.8	53	127.4	80	176.0
-27	-16.6	0	32.0	27	80.6	54	129.2	81	177.8
-26	-14.8	1	33.8	28	82.4	55	131.0	82	179.6
-25	-13.0	2	35.6	29	84.2	56	132.8	83	181.4
-24	-11.2	3	37.4	30	86.0	57	134.6	84	183.2

DEGREES CENTIGRADE TO FAHRENHEIT

°C	°F	°C	°F	°C	°F	°C	°F	°C	°F
85	185.0	112	233.6	139	282.2	166	330.8	193	379.4
86	186.8	113	235.4	140	284.0	167	332.6	194	381.2
87	188.6	114	237.2	141	285.5	168	334.4	195	383.0
88	190.4	115	239.0	142	287.6	169	336.2	196	384.8
89	192.2	116	240.8	143	289.4	170	338.0	197	386.6
90	194.0	117	242.6	144	291.2	171	339.8	198	388.4
91	195.8	118	244.4	145	293.0	172	341.6	199	390.2
92	197.6	119	246.2	146	294.8	173	343.4	200	392.0
93	199.4	120	248.0	147	296.6	174	345.2	201	393.8
94	201.2	121	249.8	148	298.4	175	347.0	202	395.6
95	203.0	122	251.6	149	300.2	176	348.8	203	397.4
96	204.8	123	253.4	150	302.0	177	350.6	204	399.2
97	206.6	124	255.2	151	303.8	178	352.4	205	401.0
98	208.4	125	257.0	152	305.6	179	354.2	206	402.8
99	210.2	126	258.8	153	307.4	180	356.0	207	404.6
100	212.0	127	260.6	154	309.2	181	357.8	208	406.4
101	213.8	128	262.4	155	311.0	182	359.6	209	408.2
102	215.6	129	264.2	156	312.8	183	361.4	210	410.0
103	217.4	130	266.0	157	314.6	184	363.2	215	419.0
104	219.2	131	267.8	158	316.4	185	365.0	220	428.0
105	221.0	132	269.6	159	318.2	186	366.8	225	437.0
106	222.8	133	271.4	160	320.0	187	368.6	230	446.0
107	224.6	134	273.2	161	321.8	188	370.4	235	455.0
108	226.4	135	275.0	162	323.6	189	372.2	240	464.0
109	228.2	136	276.8	163	325.4	190	374.0	245	473.0
110	230.2	137	278.6	164	327.2	191	375.8	250	482.0
111	231.8	138	280.4	165	329.0	192	377.6	260	500.0

ALCOHOL DILUTION TABLE - TABLE F

This is a handy table for mixing your own liquors to a desired strength. For instance, if you have 190 proof alcohol, and wish to cut it down to a 90 proof vodka, then use the 190 column under Proof Of Uncut Liquor heading. Go down this column until you arrive at your Desired Proof reading the 90 proof. The column entry at that point reads 118.0. This is the number if units of water (by volume) that you will need to add to 100 units of your uncut 190 proof to obtain the desired 90 proof vodka.

PROOF OF UNCUT LIQUOR

Distilled Proof	190 %	188 %	184 %	180 %	170 %	160 %	150 %	140 %	130 %	120 %	110 %	100 %
180	6.4	5.1	2.5									
170	13.3	11.9	9.2	6.58								
160	20.9	19.5	16.6	13.8	6.83							
150	29.5	27.9	24.9	21.9	14.5	7.2						
140	39.1	37.5	35.9	34.2	23.1	15.3	7.64					
130	50.2	48.4	45.0	41.5	33.0	24.6	16.4	8.15				
120	63.0	61.2	57.3	53.6	44.2	35.4	26.5	17.6	8.76			
110	78.0	76.0	71.9	67.8	57.9	48.0	38.3	28.6	19.0	9.5		
100	95.9	93.6	89.2	84.8	73.9	63.1	52.4	41.7	31.3	20.5	10.4	
90	118	115	110	105	93.3	81.3	64.5	57.8	48.0	34.5	22.9	11.4
80	144	142	136	131	117	104	90.8	77.6	64.5	51.4	38.5	25.6
70	179	176	169	163	148	133	118	103	88.0	72.0	56.3	43.6
60	224	221	213	206	189	171	154	136	119	102	85.0	67.5
50	287	283	275	266	245	224	204	273	162	142	121	101
40	382	377	366	356	330	304	277	253	227	200	176	150
30	540	533	519	505	471	437	403	369	335	300	267	234

REFERENCE A

DIRECTOR & REGIONAL DIRECTORS AND REGIONS COVERED for the Bureau of Alcohol Tobacco & Firearms (BATF). The local regions may change from time to time but the National address will always get to the right party even if the address might change.

Director
Office of the Director
Bureau of Alcohol, Tobacco & Firearms
1200 Pennsylvania Ave. N.W., Rm 4000
Washington, DC 20226

NORTH ATLANTIC (Connecticut, Maine, Massachusetts, New Hampshire, New York, Puerto Rico, Rhode Island, Vermont, Virgin Islands)

Regional Director
P.O. Box 15, Church St. Station
New York, NY 10008

MID ATLANTIC: (Delaware, DC, Maryland, New Jersey, Pennsylvania, Virginia)

Regional Director
2 Penn Center Plaza, Rm 360
Philadelphia, PA 19102

SOUTHEAST: (Alabama, Florida, Georgia, Mississippi, North Carolina, South Carolina, Tennessee)

Regional Director
P.O. Box 2994
Atlanta, GA 30301

CENTRAL: (Indiana, Kentucky, Michigan, ohio, W. Virginia)

Regional Director
550 Main St.
Cincinnati, OH 45202

MIDWEST: (Illinois, Iowa, Kansas, Minnesota, Missouri, Nebraska, N. Dakota, S. Dakota, Wisconsin)

Regional Director
230 S. Dearborn St., 15th floor
Chicago, IL 60604

WEST: (Alaska, Arizona, California, Hawaii, Idaho, Montana, Nevada, Oregon, Utah, Washington)

Regional Director
525 Market St. 34th floor
San Francisco, CA 94105

SOUTHWEST: (Arkansas, Colorado, Louisiana, New Mexico, Oklahoma, Texas, Wyoming)

Regional Director
Main Tower, Room 345
1200 Main St.
Dallas, TX 75202

REFERENCE B

SAMPLE LETTER TO THE BATF REQUESTING A STILL PERMIT

Address your letter (see Reference A) and then in large capital letters under this title put "GASOHOL" and then the rest of the address. Or you can address it to the Regional Regulatory Administrator. In any event they will be able to sort it out to the right department when they receive it. - (be sure to include your full address and phone number somewhere on the letter).

Date ----------

Sirs,

    I wish to obtain an experimental permit to produce Methanol for fuel. I intend to use carbohydrates of all types to ferment and will initially use conventional distilling techniques. After acquiring experience I hope to develop my own superior design(s).

    I understand I am to keep a complete record of my production and its ultimate use. I will purchase a bond or post a cash bond if necessary and I understand this bond is not large for this type of permit. I will comply with all laws including environmental and pollution statutes. I will not sell or drink any of the Ethanol so produced. I am enclosing a legal description of my premises and my initial equipment plans.

Sincerely yours

REFERENCE C

WANT MORE INFORMATION??

There are a number of Government agencies and private groups that are more than willing to share with you their experience with GASOHOL and Ethanol fermentation and distillation. Some of these are given below.

FARM ORGANIZATIONS

American Farm Bureau Federation
225 Touhy Ave.
Park Ridge, IL 60068

Agriculture Council of America
1625 Eye St. NW Suite 708
Washington, DC 20006

National Corn Growers Assn.
815 Office Park Rd. Ste. 201
West Des Moines, IA 50265

National Farmers Organization
720 Davis Ave.
Corning, IA 50841

National Farmers Union
12025 E. 45th Ave.
Denver, CO 80251

UNIVERSITIES

Send to the STATE AGRICULTURAL COLLEGE for your state. This will usually be the University that has the Designation STATE in its name. For instance in Ohio there are both an Ohio University in Columbus, Ohio. In Oklahoma there is an Oklahoma University in Norman, Oklahoma, and a Oklahoma State University in Stillwater,

Oklahoma. In both cases the university with STATE in its name is the agricultural universities (land grant colleges) address your letter as follows:

College of Agriculture
GASOHOL
------------ State University
City------------ , State------------ , Zip------------

If you do not know the location of your State university, look in the back of any MERRIAM WEBSTERS NEW COLLEGIATE DICTIONARY. There is a section entitled Colleges & Universities that will give you the name and the city and state. Fortunately colleges don't pick up and move too often.

GOVERNMENT AGENCIES

USDA
Secretary of Agriculture
14th St. & Independence Ave. SW
Washington, DC 20250

USDA
Farmers Home Administration
14th St. & Independence Ave. SW
Washington, DC 20250

Office of Energy
Office of the Secretary
U.S. Department of Agriculture
Washington, DC 20250

Ministry of Agriculture & Food
222 McIntyre St. W.
North Bay, Ontario, Canada P1B 2Y8

The U.S. Government publishes and reproduces a good many excellent up-to-the-minute pamphlets and brochures at modest cost. It may take some doing, however, to locate the correct document listings for you to choose from. It is worth the effort. Send to:

U.S. Government Publications
Washington DC 20250

Write to the AGRICULTURE department of your state at the state capitol. The following address should get your letter to the correct office:

(your state) DEPARTMENT OF AGRICULTURE
GASOHOL
City.. State.. Zip

(example: California Dept. of Agriculture)

OTHER ORGANIZATIONS AND SUPPLIERS

Home Wine & Beer Trade Assoc.
c/o Beverage Communicator
5 Barker Avenue
While Plains NY 10530

Miles Laboratories
Elkhart, IN 46514

Noguska, LLC
741 N. Countyline St.
Fostoria, OH 44830

National Gasohol Commission
521 S. 14th St. Ste. 5
Lincoln, NE 68508

Below is the Index for The Lore of Still Building, the format is as follows:

Example: 8-2 = Chapter 8 Paragraph 2
Example: T5-2 = Chapter 5 Table 2
Example: F5-1 = Chapter 5 Figure 1